CONQUEROR OF MOUNT McKINLEY

HUDSON STUCK

Born: November 11, 1863
Died: October 10, 1920

Hudson Stuck had always hoped to be the first man
ever to scale Mount McKinley, the tallest mountain
in North America. His epic ascent of that mountain
at the age of fifty, through storms and over glaciers
in an ordeal that lasted eleven weeks, is one of the
most gripping adventures in a life full of adventure.
As a young man he left his native England and
landed in Texas where he became a cowboy, a
schoolteacher and finally was ordained an Episcopal
priest, in time becoming Dean of St. Matthew's Cathedral in Dallas. Then at the age of forty he received permission to become a missionary in the
untamed wilderness of Alaska. Traveling thousands
of miles by dogsled, he established schools and hospitals for the Indians and Eskimos, and opposed all
the forces that exploited his adopted people. Whenever time allowed, he climbed mountains and lived
to see a dream come true when he conquered Mount
McKinley.

Books by Edward A. Herron

DIMOND OF ALASKA
  Adventurer in the Far North

FIRST SCIENTIST OF ALASKA
  William Healey Dall

WINGS OVER ALASKA
  The Story of Carl Ben Eielson

ALASKA'S RAILROAD BUILDER
  Mike Heney

DYNAMITE JOHNNY O'BRIEN
  Alaska's Sea Captain

CONQUEROR OF MOUNT McKINLEY
  Hudson Stuck

CONQUEROR OF
MOUNT McKINLEY
HUDSON STUCK

by Edward A. Herron

JULIAN MESSNER, INC.
NEW YORK

Published by Julian Messner, Inc.
8 West 40th Street, New York 18

Published simultaneously in Canada
by The Copp Clark Publishing Co. Limited

Printed in the United States of America

Library of Congress Catalog Card No. 64–11818

"I would rather climb that mountain
than discover the richest gold mine in Alaska."

Hudson Stuck
Archdeacon of the Yukon

CONQUEROR OF
MOUNT McKINLEY

HUDSON STUCK

1

Hudson Stuck tripped on the bottom step of the companion-way and sprawled headlong on the wooden deck. Behind him other emigrants crowded forward. A heavy boot struck his leg, and he rolled over quickly, struggling upright.

On that gloomy February evening in 1885, the ship's hold was plunged in darkness. Hudson reached out, trying to find a clear space. He felt as though he were being forced deep into a barrel, that at any moment a lid would come crashing down and he would be imprisoned, hapless cargo being carried out to sea.

Suitcases and the round, corded weight of blanket rolls struck against him as their owners floundered into the sleeping quarters.

"If you'll wait just a minute," he called, "I'll strike a match."

"Strike away, so we can see the pigsty where we'll be spending the next three months."

Hudson rasped the round head of the match on the sole of his shoe; the yellow light flared raggedly. His heart sank. Wooden bunks were stacked one upon the other from the deck to the overhead. The passageways were so narrow one would have to turn sideways in order to squeeze by. The match flared, spluttered, then went out.

"They can't treat Englishmen like this," a voice called out angrily. "I'm getting off."

"You'll have to swim back," another answered in the darkness. "There's three miles of ocean back to shore."

"What did you expect?" another voice boomed. "Travel in a royal suite?"

Another match flared and the flame was held to the wick of an oil lamp. A dull yellow glow settled over the hold. Hudson picked up his shining new bag and his blanket roll and squeezed through a passageway to the farthest corner. Instinctively he tried to keep away from the rough men crowded about him.

I'll get used to it, he told himself, as he crawled into a bunk. His head was pressing against the headboard and his shoes were flat against the wood rail at the end. He was not tall—less than five feet nine inches—yet he was unable to stretch full out. He looked around at the 140 men who were beginning to fill every available space. The tall men, he thought, would be bent like acrobats within the bunks.

He felt beneath him. The straw mattress was damp and moldy. Tiny drops of moisture were collecting on the beams overhead. Even in the yellow glow of the oil lamps he could make out the green fingers of dampness that encompassed the dark hold.

So intent had he been on examining his surroundings that he had forgotten his ancient enemy. He coughed suddenly and tried to choke back the helpless spasm that racked him. He lunged forward into a half-upright position while he held his breath. The blood pounded in his temples. The effort was useless. He coughed harshly and continuously.

When the spell was over he sagged back on the bunk, breathing heavily. It was only then that he became aware of the rhythmic, rolling motion of the ship.

I'll not die in England, he thought. I'll live until I see Australia.

"You sick, son?"

Hudson looked up at the quiet inquiry. Stretched out in the opposite bunk, separated only by eighteen inches of space from his own, was a dim figure. He could see a chain that led from crossed wrists to a ring bolted to a beam overhead.

"Lunger, eh?" The flat figure posed a second question.

Hudson winced. Tuberculosis was common in fog-ridden England, and those condemned to inevitable death from the disease were dismissed with the curt word.

"Well," the voice continued from the semidarkness, "there's all kinds of ways of dying. You got yours. I got mine." The chain rattled as the big form turned in the bunk.

The ship fell into the trough of a wave and slewed sideways viciously. Hudson was rolled violently and only saved himself from tumbling on the deck by grasping the upright that held his bunk. Across the way the man was thrown completely outward, and dangled with his full weight dragging on his chained wrists.

Hudson leaped from his bunk. He pushed and tugged, helping as the man twisted about and hauled himself into the bunk again. "I'm sorry. Why?—"

"I'm a prisoner. The guards chained me so I wouldn't run away. The Army is sending me back to Australia to hang."

"Oh—" The reticence that was instinctive with Hudson held back his questions. He started to climb into his own bunk, then hesitated. "Can I bring you something? A cup of water?"

13

"No."

Rebuffed by the curt refusal, Hudson stretched out again on the bunk. He shivered. With great difficulty he untied the blanket roll. Must be raining, he thought.

All his life he had associated rain with discomfort. He had no great affection for London where he and his older sister, Caroline, grew up among the dull red brick buildings of Paddington. It seemed to him that his childhood had been inseparably entwined with low fog and dreary, never-ending rain.

Ten years before, when he was only twelve, the cold dampness had brought on his interminable cough. Tuberculosis had come almost as a matter of course.

He remembered the first visits to a doctor who looked at him in tired discouragement. His mouth still puckered in disgust at the remembrance of the first bitter draughts of medicine. His revolt against these daily doses was the beginning of a silent rebellion that he kept locked within himself. There was no one with whom he shared his resentment.

Every form of physical activity was shut off from him. He turned to his books, closing his ears to the screaming youngsters who crowded the streets and the vacant lots that served as soccer fields.

His parents were Presbyterians, and, outwardly obedient, he attended services regularly, but only to placate them. He sat unmoving during the lengthy services, while the words and the hymns rolled past him, almost ignored. His mind, restless, inquisitive, galloped far beyond the small church.

At King's College in London he was labeled as brilliant, but always those who gave him the compliment had a depressing tone in their voices as though giving credit to one who had not long to live.

He tried to cloak his loneliness in a mantle of aloofness,

sharing confidence with no one. He walked by the banks of the river, his head high, his lips firm. But when the hockey players and the soccer players raced by him to the wild excitement of the fields, he turned and watched enviously.

The loneliness became overpowering, and he left school and returned to his home in Paddington. For more than a month he shut himself in his room. He was in rebellion against everything about him, and it was with difficulty that he restrained his impatience with the quiet queries of his father and the worried ministrations of his mother. He had to leave England, he told himself. Go far away to one of the colonies.

A notice appeared in the newspaper, telling of a Civil Service examination for a clerk's position in the Foreign Office. Duty would be in Melbourne, Australia. This was his chance!

He walked almost five miles to Whitehall to the government offices that stood so forbidding behind high iron gates. On his way he responded to a sudden impulse and entered the dim confines of St. Paul's Cathedral. There he knelt and prayed. "God, in this one thing, if it is Your will, give me success." He shivered slightly with the chill of the centuries in the cathedral. When he walked out into the rain, the organist, in practice session, let loose a torrent of music.

Hudson took the examination almost in despair. Perhaps, he thought, in this one endeavor I can repay my parents for their patient understanding.

Two weeks later the important stiff brown envelope arrived in the mail. He had led the entire group of applicants in all the subjects but one. His handwriting was illegible. In those pretypewriter days it was a fatal defect. His application was rejected.

That night his father came to his room, and pressed some

gold sovereigns into his hand. "They will buy your passage to Australia," he said. "Go with our blessing."

Now launched on the voyage, Hudson thought of the scene on the dock less than an hour before. He remembered his father's tight handclasp and his mother's tears. "I'll get well in Australia," he reassured her. Looking at his father he added, "I'm sorry I failed you two."

"Don't talk like that," Mr. Stuck said gruffly. "You didn't fail."

Hudson shook his hand for the last time. He embraced his mother, kissed Caroline briefly, then lifted his bag and went up the wooden gangplank.

He had never before been to sea. Suddenly, he was aware of the rolling motion of the ship. He concentrated on the heaving and falling. He fell into a troubled sleep.

Suddenly he bolted upright, clutched his hand to his mouth and lurched out of the bunk. He fought his way blindly along the obstructing passageway, stumbling up the steep companionway to the open deck, and raced blindly to the rail. He hung over it, weak and exhausted, scarcely conscious of the hissing waves that came within inches of his face.

He was sick through most of the voyage. The ship followed a curious but not uncommon course on the planned route to Australia. It turned westward across the Atlantic to call first at American ports on the Gulf of Mexico before heading south again on the long journey to the distant colony.

As the ship plowed steadily westward Hudson became more and more acquainted with the prisoner.

"Bristol's the name, John Bristol. I was younger than you when I first left England. That was nineteen years ago." Stretched out on the bunk, deftly countering every battering motion of the wind and waves, he continued speaking quietly.

He told how as a boy of seventeen, he had gone with his father from England to Australia, joining the wild rush of gold hunters. The gold fever had subsided, and when the fortune hunters sought to take up land for homesteads in New South Wales, the privilege had been denied them. Bristol, young and excitable, had led an uprising of gold hunters against the troops stationed at Ballarat. Thirty-four of the prospectors and four of the soldiers had been killed.

Bristol had escaped from Australia and sailed as a seaman into every corner of the world. Then a desire to see his homeland had overcome his good judgment. He had returned to England, been recognized, seized and condemned to return to Australia to be hanged.

It was on April 1, 1885, almost fifty days out of England that Hudson and the emigrants first saw the faint green smudge marking the shore line of Texas.

"That'll be the port of Indianola," John Bristol remarked. "I was in this part of the world years ago."

"There's a boat coming out," Hudson said, pointing.

The small rowboat pulled steadily from the wooden wharves, but instead of coming alongside, the rowers rested on their oars and kept a distance from the emigrant ship. A portly figure in an immaculate white suit stood uncertainly in the bow, his hand held as though in warning.

"There's yellow fever ashore!" he shouted. "Turn around and go back!"

The captain screamed at him. "That's impossible! We need provisions—water!"

"You've been warned!" the voice boomed back at him. "Come ashore at your peril!"

Ignoring the warning, the captain steered the ship determinedly to the wharf. As though on signal, the emigrants who had been lining the rail rushed at him and knocked him down. "We're not going in there!" one of them yelled. "We're not dying of yellow fever!"

"We've got to have food and water!" the captain screamed. "We can't leave without—"

At that moment a surge of current took hold of the ship, and moved it sluggishly away from land. It had gone scarcely a hundred yards when it stuck on a sand bar. Then the vessel moved around drunkenly, shook loose from the bar and started to slide back toward the waiting sea.

Bristol, still in chains, but free to walk the decks, strode to the rail. He looked at the men grouped about. He looked beyond them to Hudson Stuck. Then, without another word he leaped overboard.

Hudson followed him into the muddy water. He started choking and sputtering. Then he felt hands around his shoulder. "Swim, Hudson! Swim."

Hudson choked on the water. "I can't!"

"Idiot!" Bristol thrust out his chained wrists, grabbed Hudson by the shoulder, and began to swim against the strong current.

Coughing and gagging, Hudson Stuck touched shore on America.

He dragged himself weakly through the swamp grasses, following the bulk of John Bristol, outlined in the darkness just ahead of him. The croaking of frogs came in a shrill, unending chorus. Bristol stood upright.

"Why did you do it?" he demanded.

"I thought you'd drown," Hudson said, pointing to the chains.

Bristol snorted. "Well, now, how are you going to get back to that ship?"

"I'm not. I don't care where I go. Texas, Australia. It makes no difference. I'm going to die anyhow."

"Stop that nonsense. You're not going to die." Bristol looked at the chains on his wrists. "Not if I can get these off."

They found a fisherman who silently and methodically sawed the chains on Bristol's wrists. "If you're running away," he said without lifting his head, "San Antonio is north."

Early the next morning when Hudson and Bristol forced their way through the underbrush they found the black dirt road leading north. It ran flat and almost unbending, for there were few hills to bar the way. It was deserted, as though the entire world had drawn back from the fever-stricken town.

They were an odd pair, Hudson, thin, almost gaunt, his beard a patch of reddish fuzz on his chin; Bristol, a broad-shouldered giant, his beard a huge black forest that gave him a fierce piratelike look.

During the first mile Hudson had tripped and torn a seam of his tight-fitting English trousers. When he protested at the result, Bristol snorted, "If you've got any sense, you'll tear out the other seam, too. Let a little blood circulate around those skinny legs. And it's going to get hot."

Steaming humid stickiness enveloped them as they tramped through the tunnels of tangled green in the swamplands of southern Texas. The winding road was bordered with giant oak trees bent over with long beards of Spanish moss.

To Hudson, only seven weeks removed from the crowded streets of London, this America was a deserted land. They passed a few clearings in which sagging log cabins squatted on small hills to keep away from the encroaching swamps. Most of the cabins were deserted, as though the terror spreading from Indianola had touched even the distant clearings.

But as they drew farther from the coast town, they began to meet a few people on the road, though these were silent and fearful, as though distrusting anyone coming from the direction of the fever-stricken port.

Hudson looked at the strangers with curiosity. Like most Englishmen, educated and noneducated alike, he knew very little about America and Americans. He had been born at a time when the Civil War was at its height, at the Battle of Gettysburg, yet even in his early school years he had no recollection of studying about the new land. The world for him, and for most Englishmen, was confined to the home islands and the British colonies spread like jewels around the entire world. America was an empty phrase from his history book, a land that had foolishly broken away from the family of colonies.

But history was far from his mind as he trudged through the land. He was caught in adventure, and all of it centered around the most fabulous man he had ever met, John Bristol.

The big seaman seemed to have a sixth sense for survival. He fashioned a hook from a piece of scrap metal, and a line from a drooping vine, and with them he pulled catfish from the murky waters. The first night he made bedding from the dried moss and they slept in the open. When rain threatened, on the second night, he summoned unexpected charm and persuaded a reluctant farmer to permit the two wanderers to sleep under the shelter of a crude shed. In the cold morning he insisted upon repaying the hospitality with offers of odd jobs about the farm.

The two walked north for four days. The coastal lowlands changed to sloping prairie that was sometimes choked with thorny mesquite. On the evening of the fourth day they crested a slight rise and saw before them the tightly packed city of San Antonio, where nearly fifteen thousand Americans,

Mexicans and European emigrants were living by the banks of the swift San Antonio River. Far to the north there was a shield of mountains.

When they entered the town, walking past the limestone homes of the German settlers, Hudson saw a sudden change come over Bristol. He became suspicious, alert, fearful that his identity might be discovered.

It was only when they had gone beyond, into the square of the Alamo, the Mexican quarters, that Bristol relaxed. Hudson gazed at the windowless cabins of stakes and adobe. Never before had he seen anything like these. Horsemen rode in the street, and the sidewalks were crowded with men who carried side arms as though they were part of their clothing.

They crossed the bridge and walked down Commerce Street, lined with American-style wooden homes surrounded by gardens. The main square was crowded with hotels and glass-fronted stores. Hudson looked longingly at the hotel.

"I'd like very much to get a bath."

"The river'll do for you, son. We've got to find a job quickly."

Within the hour they were rubbing down teams of mules, just returned from hauling a wagon train from a settlement to the west of San Antonio.

They stayed there for a week, then, because Bristol had displayed a great dexterity in handling the nervous animals, the two were signed on as drivers in a train of eight wagons rolling for 120 miles through the dried prairie to Junction City.

There were ten mules dragging each heavily loaded wagon. For the first few hours Hudson sat by Bristol's side, watching intently as the big man urged the skittish animals onward. Then he, in turn, took the thick bundle of leather reins and discovered almost to his amazement that the animals responded.

There were other lessons that Bristol taught Hudson during the slow, leisurely eight-day trip to Junction City. He taught him to use a rifle, and cheered when the lanky youth brought down one of the scores of jack rabbits that were always seen bouncing in the brush. Then additional lessons followed in the skinning and cooking of the tough-meated animals.

"You've taught me a lot," Hudson said admiringly.

"Not much good it's done me," Bristol replied. "If I had any sense I'd be owning a wagon train like this—growing up with a new country." He became moody and depressed, and Hudson moved away, leaving the older man to his bitter thoughts.

At night they slept beneath the wagons. The weather was suspiciously warm for April. Soft winds came from the western deserts.

One night Hudson woke when a chill breeze raced down on them. He sat upright, and the movement woke Bristol. Suddenly there was a burst of furious sound and a gale of wind screamed around them, a viciously cold, biting wind. "It's a norther," Bristol called. "We better shake out of here. It'll be freezing in ten minutes!"

They hitched up the mules, cracked the whip and drove pell-mell over the prairie to Junction City.

When they were safely under shelter, Bristol shook the ice from his beard. "That's the end of that," he announced. "One of the other drivers tells me there's a rancher looking for hands." He looked at Hudson critically. "How'd you like to become a cowboy?"

Two months from the day he left his London home, Hudson Stuck was astride a horse, nudging a reluctant cow down to the herd that was wading into Maynard Creek. Far to his left he could see John Bristol, a giant astride a small pony. Hudson waved to him, spoke to his horse and hung on awkwardly.

He was a London cowboy in Texas.

2

Hudson became passionately fond of horses. Each morning he and Bristol rose before dawn, ate a huge breakfast, then rode across the wide, flat prairie to the waiting herds.

To Hudson it seemed as though all his life he had been waiting to sit astride a swift horse, feeling the wind rushing against his cheek, listening to the distant lulling of the herd.

He had never before known such freedom. He forgot the paved streets and brick pavements of London, the ominous buildings that had encircled him all of his life.

At night, when they returned to the ranch, he was almost reluctant to turn the animal loose for the night in the corral. When he slept, it was grudgingly, because it was a time of inaction. Yet when his head touched the pillow, he slept soundly, worn out with the day's activities.

John Bristol eyed him approvingly. "Too bad you didn't get to do this five years sooner, Hudson. That cough wouldn't have gotten such a hold on you."

"Bother the cough," Hudson said irritably. "I'd forgotten about it until you mentioned it." It was true. On the dry open spaces of Texas the cough had begun to disappear. He was clear eyed. His chest was still sunken, but his stride was becoming more vigorous.

In all the time he had been gone, except for fleeting moments as he fell off to sleep, he felt no pangs of homesickness. England and his parents seemed to exist only in a distant dream. He had to force himself to write and tell them where he was and what he was doing.

With one exception, the men about him were entirely different from those he had known in England. Yankee Bundy, the owner of the ranch was, as far as Hudson could determine, a man with only one thought in mind—to amass wealth in a great hurry before going back to a distant part of New England from which he had come.

His partner, John Patterson, was a Scotsman. In him, Hudson was faintly reminded of the men he had known in London. The rest of the ranch hands were Mexicans. On these good-natured people he tried out the Spanish he had learned in school, and discovered, to his amazement, that they were able to understand him, and he, in a stumbling way, to understand them. He looked upon the Mexicans with an affection that he had so far denied to others. It was a trait that was to be with him throughout his life—a harsh impatience for those of his own station in life, a strong sympathy and understanding for those who were less fortunate.

John Bristol, noting his friendship with the Mexican ranch hands, asked, "If you want to help those people, Hudson, why don't you teach them how to read and write English?" Hudson nodded in agreement.

From that time on, when he finished his evening meal, he strode over to the bunkhouse where the Mexican hands were gathered. With the three or four who were interested he sat in the corner, under a fitful yellow kerosene lamp, and patiently taught them the alphabet. For most of them it was the first attempt anyone had ever made to teach them to read or write.

It was a simple problem in arithmetic that caused Hudson Stuck to turn from the carefree life he had on Bundy's ranch. His salary each month was ten dollars. But when, on payday, the thrifty Bundy subtracted nickles and dimes and quarters and then full dollars for tobacco, laundry, new shirts and new boots, Hudson discovered that his earnings at the end of each month would sometimes be as low as three or four dollars. He looked at the money disconsolately. John Bristol noted his discouragement.

"Lad, you're having a grand time, but you'll never get rich as a ranch hand at Bundy's."

"What about you?" Hudson demanded. "You don't seem to be worried about the lack of money."

"You've forgotten, lad, you and I have different goals. I'm looking for a place to stay in safety. The money will come later. But you can't go on like this. You've got to find yourself a goal here in Texas. Look, lad," and he pointed to Bundy and Patterson huddled over the set of ledgers in the distant end of the bunkhouse. "Those two, mark my words, will be wealthy within fifteen years. Every dollar they get their hands on they use to buy more land. They've found the secret. Buy up this prairie, stock it with cattle, let the cattle increase— and wealth will come. Give it some thought, Hudson. You can't be a cowboy forever."

But Hudson put the thought out of his mind. He gave himself up entirely to riding, hunting, fishing. He led a carefree life without thought for the future. It was only when the spring came that he realized ruefully he would have to make a move to try to better himself.

The money he had saved almost disappeared when he purchased a horse from Bundy which he named Gotch. It was almost his sole possession when he left the ranch in search of his fortune.

Bristol remained behind. "Write to me, lad; let me know how it goes with you."

Hudson rode off into the hot sun. Behind him trotted a nondescript dog whom he called Capitan. He turned once to wave good-by to John, then rode steadily, stopping only to rest his horse or gnaw at the sandwiches John had pressed on him at parting.

He had no destination in mind, loving only the comfortable feel of the horse beneath him and the wide, flat landscape that stretched around and beyond.

Once he stayed at a ranch for a week while he rode the fence line, repairing it. At another ranch he helped with the annual sheep dip, being paid one dollar a day to herd the bawling sheep down the runway where they splashed through the odorous disinfectant.

His money was disappearing rapidly. Finally he was unable to purchase feed for the horse. He realized it would be impossible for him to continue.

By chance he heard that the telegraph company needed a man to repair the line that had been battered by a vicious windstorm. Hudson rode breathlessly to the telegraph office and secured the job that paid two dollars and fifty cents a day. He was handed a set of climbing spurs, a hammer, pliers, insulators, a length of rope and was told to start immediately.

He galloped at breakneck speed over the sun-drenched prairie, with only the unwavering line of telegraph poles as a guide. When he came to a break in the wire, he looped the rope about the broken end and tied the rope to his belt while he inched up the pole, digging the iron spurs into the wood. There he twisted the ends of wire together, repairing the break. The wooden posts were easy to climb, but the iron posts were searing hot and treacherous.

That night he slept under the stars; then he rode again through the second day, his eyes lifted to the wires humming overhead, thin black lines silhouetted against the blue sky. Toward evening, climbing down from a pole, he slipped and fell heavily, and lost consciousness.

When he awoke an older man was bending over him. Seeing the broad, ruddy face, for a moment Hudson thought that by some miracle he had been transported home to London. When the stranger spoke, and he recognized the familiar clipped accents, he was even more sure of a miracle.

"You've had a bad fall, lad. Fortunate for you I came along when I did. The coyotes were getting curious."

Hudson struggled upright. "Who are you?" he demanded.

The stranger ignored the rudeness. "My name is Johnson, James Steptoe Johnson. I'm the Episcopalian bishop of West Texas. And who are you?"

"Hudson Stuck, sir. Forgive me. It's just that I was startled —waking up and seeing you!"

"Let's get you to town. Can you mount?"

Together they rode over the darkened prairie into the town, Hudson speaking rapidly, excitedly, pouring out words as though he had thirsted for this chance meeting. All the reservation that had been bottled up within him welled out, and he found relief in talking of England with an Englishman. Bishop Johnson was equally delighted. "Texas could use more young men like you," he commented. "Educated men. Although you seem to have taken well to the cowboy role in Texas."

"I love to ride," Hudson replied. He looked to the faintly humming lines overhead. "But I've climbed my last telegraph pole. I'm not ready to break my neck yet. No," he said emphatically, "I've got to find another job."

"Are you interested in schoolteaching? Would it bore you?"

"Not if I were sure of my next meal."

"At Rocksprings there are some ranchers who are trying to start a school for their children. If you wish, I could give you a note, recommending you."

"I'll try it," Hudson said simply. "Thank you."

Back in town he received five dollars for his two days of work on the telegraph line. His clothing was ragged, and he knew he would present a sorry sight when he applied for the teaching position. Sorrowfully he decided to sell Gotch, and with the money he purchased a suit of clothing. That night, because he could not afford to pay fifty cents for a hotel room, he crept into the livery stable and slept in the straw.

Early in the morning he started walking the thirty-eight miles to Rocksprings. He was hot and exhausted when he stood before the rancher who was to do the hiring for the school, and heard his hesitant words, "Tell you what, son, I'd like to talk it over with the other parents. You come back, say in four days."

Hudson turned and walked with firm strides down the road. He was too proud to tell the rancher that he had not eaten since sunrise and that he would be forced to sleep on the open prairie that night.

He waited in town, almost panic-stricken as his money reached the vanishing point. On the morning of the fourth day, long before the sun had climbed over the rim of the prairie, he slipped down to the creek and washed his one shirt. Then he carried it in his arms like a flag, drying it in the warm morning sun as he strode hastily along the road back to Rocksprings.

This time four of the ranchers and their wives were waiting for him, sitting solemnly on the porch of the ranch house, looking at him almost with suspicion.

"You're English, huh, son?"

"Yes, I am." Hudson fought the growing feeling of irritability that welled up in him. What was wrong with being an Englishman?

"You understand we want just plain learning for the young ones? Their numbers, a bit of spelling, and lots of reading. Nothing fancy like I hear you fellows over there—"

Hudson bit his lips to keep from snapping back at his inquisitor. He was hungry. If he was to eat that night he must— "Nothing fancy, of course," he told them. "Solid grounding in the numbers, competition to develop good spellers, and emphasis on group reading aloud."

They nodded approval. There were some whispered remarks, then one of the ranchers held out his hand. "All right, Stuck, you're the new teacher at Rocksprings. The pay is forty dollars a month, and you'll board around, starting at my house. I'm Jim Settles. The school room'll be on my place. We've cleaned out a corner in the barn, and you'll be right comfortable. Good luck."

Fifteen children, ranging in age from eight to sixteen, were waiting, and Hudson started classes within the hour. The pupils were seated on hard wooden benches placed around the sides of the hastily cleared harness room. Each one clutched a *Blue Back Speller* and a *McGuffey's Reader* as though they were prized possessions. Outside a dozen horses, dozing in the sun, were tied to a rail. They waited until the children would come and ride them back to their ranch corrals.

When Hudson saw the bright-eyed, healthy youngsters, he thought almost enviously of his own childhood in the rain-drenched streets of London. He frowned, and the students were immediately aware of his mood. They seemed to shrivel a bit in terrified expectancy. Then one boy forced a smile and walked hesitantly toward Hudson, his hand outstretched. "I'm one of the Settles boys. I'm Ron. Dad said I should welcome you."

Hudson grasped the small hand firmly. "Thank you." He looked over the blond head to the others. "Open your readers," he said. "We'll start at the beginning."

He was schoolmaster at Rocksprings for five months. During that time he gave himself wholeheartedly to the task before him. He had given his word to the parents of the children, and he let nothing swerve him from the task.

He wrote to John Bristol. "I like teaching. I like the children. But I can't seem to become friendly with their parents. I think they're suspicious of Englishmen. Why haven't you written?"

Before he sealed the letter, he hesitated. It was the third time he had written John with no reply. Impulsively he put a stamped envelope addressed to himself at Rocksprings in with his letter. "Now," he said in a postscript, "you've no excuse for not writing."

Within two weeks came a scrawled reply. "I've got a good horse waiting for you. I hope you are well. John Bristol."

For years to come this was to be the correspondence between the two men, long, enthusiastic letters written by Hudson, short, almost illegible notes scrawled by John Bristol.

In the spring the children were called out to help about the ranches, and the school term came to an abrupt end. The children shook hands solemnly as they slipped one by one from the school room. Hudson packed his belongings, said good-by to the Settles, then rode with one of the ranch hands back to town.

He had managed to save most of the $200 salary that had been paid him. It was the most money he had ever accumulated in all his twenty-two years.

He returned to ranching, not only because of his love for the prairies, but because of his yearning to renew his friendship with Bristol. After a few months with his friend he received a letter from Bishop Johnson telling of the need for a schoolteacher at the John C. French School in Cuero.

Once again he left Bristol for Cuero, a wild, brawling cattle town. Only a few years before Hudson's arrival, three men had been hung from a massive oak tree in the center of the town. The main street was filled, day and night, with fighting, quarrelsome cowboys readying herds for the drive east to New Orleans, or north along the Chisolm Trail to the railheads of the Middle West. During the day he frequently had to raise his voice to be heard over the mooing, bellowing cattle that shuffled in the dusty road just outside the schoolhouse.

John Bristol came through several times with herds of cattle being delivered to the buyers at Cuero. He appeared at the close of the school term and had little trouble persuading Hudson to come with him on a three-month trip up to Denver, into the Rocky Mountain country. They traveled by train to Denver where they purchased horses, then started for the wall of the mountains looming in the West.

It was on that trip that Hudson was initiated into mountain climbing. There was a sheer peak hanging over their campsite, and he looked at it longingly. "Let's leave the horses to rest," he said to Bristol. "Let's climb that mountain."

For once Bristol hung back. He looked upward, squinting

in the sun, and shook his head dubiously. "Doesn't make sense," he said. "Got good strong horses here. What's a man want to leave them for and go shinnying up a bunch of bare rocks?" He looked earnestly at Hudson. "Now tell me, what's the good of climbing up there?"

Hudson never took his gaze from the peak. "I don't know," he answered.

Bristol started to walk back to the campsite. When he saw that Hudson had not followed, he hesitated, then came back to the younger man's side. "Look. I'm getting too old for that kind of nonsense. I got some gear I want to work over. Why don't you just take off and climb anything in sight? Be back around sundown so I don't get to thinking you've been eaten up by bears."

Hudson nodded. Then, without a backward glance, he squeezed between two boulders, wedged his boot into a crevice and started inching upward. At first he was cautious, almost timid, his fingers fastening with a rigid grip for support on every intervening tree, every knob of rock.

Then he grew more confident, bolder. His pace quickened. He found footholds and handholds, pulling himself upward and upward. Several times he glanced downward, but there was no fear. He gloried in the wide spread of the world unfolding beneath him.

For hours he was alone on the mountain. When the shadows began to darken in the valleys below, he started the descent most regretfully. He kept looking across to the other peaks that soared all about him. They were alive, inviting conquest.

When they had started their return to Texas and were walking the streets of Denver, Bristol suddenly leaped away from Hudson into the shelter of a doorway.

"What is it, John? What's wrong?"

"Those people over there—" Bristol pointed to a group of well-dressed tourists. "They're English. I saw one of them looking. He may have recognized me."

"That's foolish," Hudson said. "It's been two years—"

"People have long memories," John said stubbornly. "Let's get out of here."

When they were safely away from the city, on the train taking them back to Texas, Bristol tugged at his fierce black beard and muttered, "Someday they'll find me. I'll have to leave this country."

Hudson felt a twinge of apprehension, but said nothing.

He settled down again to teaching at the grammar school in Cuero, and was soon made principal. Had Hudson elected to continue teaching, it is inevitable that his responsibilities would have increased in direct proportion to the tremendous expansion awaiting all of Texas. He would surely have become head of one of the great Texas universities.

But a far different life was waiting for him. Its course was influenced by two men—John Bristol, over whom hung a sentence of death, and James Johnson, the Episcopal bishop of West Texas. Hudson met frequently with the bishop.

He found himself being drawn more and more to the small mission that the Episcopal church maintained as an outpost in the cattle town of Cuero. Without being asked, he started to perform small tasks about the building, lighting the church for the evening services, and sweeping the floor in the mornings.

On Good Friday, in preparation for the religious observance, he draped the altar. He watched intently as Bishop Johnson, in a quiet methodical way, led the people of West Texas to a deeper realization of the presence of God.

He taught in Cuero for three years, and he drew closer and closer to the church. There was no urging on the part of the bishop, but a warm friendship developed between the older man and the young drifter from the streets of London who had started to put roots down into the dry soil of Texas.

For Hudson the change from the austere Presbyterian religion, the faith of his parents and of their ancestors for nearly three hundred years before, to that of the Episcopal religion was not easy. He had drifted from the practice of his faith, but the fault, during his early years in Texas, he ascribed to his wanderings. The greatest influence for the change was in the quiet, inspiring life of Bishop Johnson. Hudson reasoned that whatever attracted the wholehearted devotion of Johnson must of itself be good.

He did not walk into the new religion like a man passing through a gate into another garden. He studied it, appraised it, debated its merits within himself, then accepted it without reservation.

In the summer of 1889, when he was twenty-six years old, Hudson received permission to become a lay reader at the church, conducting services in the absence of the bishop. He taught Sunday school, again of his own accord.

Within him great decisions were being debated. He knew that to follow in the footsteps of a clergyman like Bishop Johnson would require a great deal of education, far more than he had already attained. He knew, too, with a feeling of hopelessness, that he did not have the money to pay for that education. In despair he thrust out of his mind the thought that was looming ever larger, that perhaps he should enter the Episcopal ministry.

One day while reading in Bishop Johnson's study, he saw a letter on which was attached a note, "For Hudson." He was curious and began to read the correspondence. It spoke of a fund that had been entrusted to the bishop which would permit the college education and seminary training of candidates for holy orders in the Episcopal ministry. The young men who availed themselves of this training would be guaranteed thirty dollars a month for as long a period as necessary. Their tuition would be paid at the University of the South, in Sewanee, Tennessee.

Hudson could scarcely control his eagerness. When the bishop came to the study, he leaped to his feet with the letter in his hand.

"Bishop," Hudson said, "this is what I have been wanting to talk to you about; how I could possibly raise the money in order to attend the seminary."

Bishop Johnson smiled. "I believe with all my heart that you should be one of us. I wanted the first word, Hudson, to come from you. If this letter is the key, then we should both thank God for it. Sit down. Let me tell you about the University of the South."

3

"Too bad you missed her." Hudson Stuck followed the stationmaster's grimy finger pointing to the snorting locomotive with its lone passenger car tailing behind. The car bent precariously around the green mountainside, then disappeared from view.

He sat wearily on his traveling bag and brushed at the dust thick on his suit.

"Traveled a good piece, friend?" the stationmaster asked solicitously.

"From Texas. I've been three days and nights on the train." He fought back the weariness, rose to his feet and lifted his bag.

"Where you going?" the stationmaster demanded.

"I'm going to walk to the university."

"But that's six miles—and its straight up the mountain!"

"I know."

"No need for you to rush off like that, friend. Tell you what. There's a string of empties going up to the mine in a few minutes. No one around here'd be mad if you hopped aboard. Goes right by the university station."

Hudson hesitated. Enter the university riding on a coal car? He took a step away, then came back. "I'll be glad to. Where are the cars?"

So it was in August, 1889, that Hudson Stuck, grimy and sooted after the slow, grinding trip up a steep mountainside, past waterfalls and along ledges overlooking distant valleys, arrived at the University of the South in Sewanee, Tennessee. He tossed his bag from the moving train and leaped after it, sprawling in the dust. He scrambled to his feet and looked about, but his arrival had been unnoticed. Quickly he picked up his battered bag and started hiking along the dirt road.

A horse and buggy clattered to a halt behind him. The colored driver leaped out and insisted that Hudson climb into the buggy. "I'm Jason, sir. You going to St. Luke's Hall? One of the theological students?"

"Yes, I am."

"Could tell. Older, sir. Not like some of them wild ones who come up to Sewanee—though they soon settle down. Mountain air. Peaceful and quietlike here." He looked sideways at Hudson. "Either settle down or go away to some other place. It's peaceful here. That's the way the reverend likes it."

"Have you been at the university for long, Jason?"

"Twenty year. Since the very day they started rebuilding, right after the war." He pointed with his buggy whip to a clump of trees. "I was right there when Bishop Quintard speaks to the professors and the students—nine of them— and they all march in the classrooms, singing hymns." He looked around proudly. "I helped clean the mess after the federal troops near ruined the place. Carted the stones of the buildings they blew up, and cut down trees and carried mortar for the new buildings—I did just about everything." He pulled back on the reins and pointed to a somber sandstone building. "That's St. Luke's Hall. I helped build it."

He carried Hudson's bag to the door. "Fine school, sir. There's no other like it in the world."

Hudson tapped hesitantly on the door knocker. When there was no answer he swung back the ponderous door and walked in. There was a clatter of footsteps on the stairs and a young man in a flowing black gown came racing downward. He stopped abruptly at the sight of Hudson.

"Sorry, sir. A bit late for class." The young man hesitated. "You're one of the new professors we've been expecting?"

Hudson shook his head. "No, I'm not. I'm one of the theological students. I'm Hudson Stuck." He held out his hand.

"And I'm Fred Olmstead. Forgive me for staring, Stuck. It's just that you're a bit older than—"

"I know," Hudson replied. "I'm an old man—twenty-six to be exact, give or take a few months."

"Forget it," Olmstead said warmly. "Let me have your bag, and I'll show you your room."

"You had a class—"

"Bother, I did! I'll have to run. Just up these stairs to the second floor. You'll find your name posted. The fellows will be coming back within an hour or so." He was halfway through the door. "There are twenty of us, you know. I mean in the theological school. Good bunch." He was gone in a flurry of black.

Hudson found his room. Without bothering to unpack, he stood at the open window and looked over the university campus. The school was almost buried in a forest of massive oak and maple trees that crowded close to the gray stone buildings. The grass that was planted in the few open spaces was parched brown, almost seared like the Texas prairie. Through the trees he could glimpse other college buildings, square and massive like those of Cambridge and Oxford back in England. Occasionally, a small wooden cottage, residence for one of the faculty, showed through the clearings. Over all was a peaceful quiet, broken only by the swift flight of birds winging between the trees.

He remembered the parting words of his friend Bishop Johnson: "You'll not find riches or power at Sewanee. It was nourished in adversity and it became vigorous in poverty. But you will find knowledge and, if you are fortunate, you will find there the reason why men are placed on earth."

Hudson started his three years of theological studies uneasily. He had written to his Presbyterian parents and to his sister Caroline, telling of his decision to study for the Episcopal ministry. He received no answer to his letters.

His studies were no problem. He returned easily to the Latin and Greek texts, and he sat, open and receptive, before the brilliant men who formed the faculty of the university. He recited clearly, calmly, and he was marked from the beginning as an exceptional student. But he was not able to mix freely with the younger men about him.

His first month went by, September came, and the leaves on the maples turned golden and drifted uncertainly to the ground. In his free time he walked alone along the trails that crisscrossed the 10,000 wooded acres of the university domain. He stood solitary and unmoving at Morgan's Steep and Polk's Lookout, staring over the valleys that dropped away from the Cumberland Plateau. In the letters he wrote to his parents he spoke only of the great peace that surrounded the university perched high on the Tennessee mountain, and of his progress in his studies. The struggles that waged within he kept secret.

He was not positive he had followed the right course. He was beset with doubts as to his ability to carry out the religious duties that he had watched Bishop Johnson perform in the small towns of West Texas.

During each siege of doubt and despair he prayed for courage to continue, and the courage was given him. He returned from his solitary walks about the mountain determined to persevere to his ordination.

In his third month at Sewanee, when the cold winter rains came, he stayed too long on the face of the mountain and contracted a chill. He became seriously ill. He was in bed, coughing almost continuously, feverish, when the wife of Dr. William Porcher DuBose, one of the faculty, came to his room.

"Hudson Stuck," she said sternly, "since you've come to Sewanee you've lived in a little world all by yourself, some place halfway between here and England. Now perhaps you'll let me break a bit into that world and nurse you back to health. After that—" she shrugged her shoulders.

For two weeks Mrs. DuBose brought him his food and medicine. Finally the racking cough quieted and he was able to move about, pale and almost wraithlike in his thinness. "Getting well isn't enough," she warned Hudson. "You'll have to change. We've watched other theological students come to the university and try to live by themselves. It doesn't work. If you're to become an Episcopal clergyman, you'll be a man of the people—and you've got to start learning how right now. Go down there and join the other young men! Go ahead!"

She almost pushed him out the door. Excited voices lifted in a shrill chorus beyond a wall of trees. A flat stretch of land that had been cleared from the forest was the setting for two teams locked in a torrid baseball game, despite the fact that the season had long since gone. There was even a hint of snow in the air. Hudson sat on the cold bench and stared in bewilderment at the players. There were few things in America that baffled him completely. Unfortunately, baseball was one of them.

He gave up his effort to grasp the meaning of all the shouting and racing about, and turned to go back to his room. But on the crest of the path leading to St. Luke's he saw Mrs. DuBose. He smiled, tipped his hat and walked to the gymnasium. Gingerly, aware of his weakness, he exercised in solitude on the homemade swings, trapeze bars, horizontal bars and parallel bars.

The next day he sought out Fred Olmstead. "I've spotted some excellent chestnut trees. Perhaps a nutting party would be in order. Would you and some of the others come with me?"

Olmstead lifted his eyes in mock amazement. "You're inviting us to go with you? Why, Stuck, we thought you were practicing to become a hermit! Of course we'll go! Just one minute until I get some of the fellows together!"

Later, he joined the Literary Society. He had a remarkable talent for writing and when he submitted an essay on Sir Walter Scott, it won him a Literary Society award. He mingled more and more with his fellow students and fitted more readily into the daily activities of the university. He was selected editor of the journal of the University of the South. When the school established its first annual, Hudson became the assistant editor.

Horses were available for hire close to the university, and Hudson persuaded Fred Olmstead to join him in riding through a wilderness almost untouched since the days of Daniel Boone. When they tired of the ocean of trees, they explored the deep caves that abounded in the region.

When the fits of moodiness returned, Hudson took his Latin and Greek textbooks and went off by himself, away from the rest of the world, except for the excited cries of birds that resented his intrusion.

He attended the exercises faithfully each day in St. Augustine's Chapel, sitting on the hard wooden benches. But his most moving prayers, his deepest meditations, came when he was alone on the mountain.

The school term at Sewanee was unlike that of other colleges. Studies started in April and continued until early December. One of the reasons was to take advantage of the comparatively cool summer offered by the high mountain plateau. The area was looked upon as a refuge during the summer months, since its elevation placed it above the "yellow fever line." But the most cogent reason for the scheduling was given by one of the founders when he said that the young men should be kept occupied with their studies during the "frivolous" warm months of the year.

Hudson watched in silent envy in December, 1889, as classmates disappeared down the hill, heading for long holidays with their families in distant cities and states. He had arranged to work during the vacation period on one of the farms in the valley lying far below the university campus. Then a letter came from Bishop Johnson. "We need your help at Cuero," he wrote. "Can you come?" Money for railroad fare was folded inside the envelope.

That same afternoon Hudson was aboard the train for the long, gritty ride back to Texas. He slept fitfully at night, stared silently out the grimy windows during the day. He swung off the train at the red brick station at Cuero, then walked along the dusty road to the bishop's residence.

At Lavaca, a small seacoast town fifty miles to the south, a series of vicious hurricanes had disheartened the Episcopal congregation, and they had left the area, abandoning the church building. "Not too much to look at on the outside,"

45

the bishop explained to Hudson, "but the interior is beautiful dark walnut paneling. It's been judged one of the best-designed small churches in this country. We intend to move the building to Cuero."

"How?"

"The railroad's offered to transport it on flatcars. Men of the parish have volunteered to help. You'll be in charge. Good luck."

For three months Hudson labored on the project, supervising the raising of the church carefully from its foundation, rolling it on elevated timbers to the railroad, easing it aboard the coupled flatcars, then shepherding it through the rolling countryside as the train puffed slowly northward. Once disaster threatened. The train came to an abrupt halt when a wheel broke. The steep-roofed church was stranded in the middle of grazing land for three days until a new wheel could be procured.

Then at Cuero, the process was reversed. The sweating, shouting, exhausted parishioners, urged on by Hudson, eased the building from the flatcars, then cracked whips over straining oxen as they pulled the church along Live Oak Street to its final resting place at Esplanade.

Hudson sank exhausted in the roadway. He forgot how tired he was when Bishop Johnson handed him a scrawled note from John Bristol. "Get yourself down to Victoria in a big hurry. I've got a surprise for you," he read.

Hudson secured permission and rode for twenty miles across the rolling prairie. Bristol was waiting when he came to Victoria. "Come along with me, son." He led him along a rutted wagon lane for five miles until they came to a small arch made of willow branches. Above it, a shingle creaked in the wind. On the shingle were carved three words— "The Blossom B."

"That's mine," he said proudly. "Forty acres, and fifteen of the scrawniest cattle you've ever seen. But they're putting on weight, and they'll mean money in the pocket, come next spring."

Hudson felt a pang of envy. Once more a wave of doubt rolled over him. Quickly he stifled his doubts and held out his hand. "I'm glad you've decided to stop running, that you're going to remain in Texas."

Hudson stayed with his friend for two weeks, then went back to his duties at Cuero. From there he returned, in March 1890, for his second year of theological studies at the university.

He volunteered to take over the direction of St. Paul's, a mission for the colored people who worked as domestics at the university. Several times each week he met with his parishioners, instructing them in the catechism of the Episcopal creed. On Sunday afternoons he held services for them in the white church. He was told to instruct students for the sacrament of Confirmation, and he plunged into the task eagerly. Just prior to the religious ceremony, he examined the applicants to see how much of the instruction they had absorbed. At the time of Confirmation he led only four applicants before the bishop.

"I had expected thirty or more for Confirmation. Where are the others?"

"They were not ready," Hudson replied. In this, as in everything he undertook, he was rigidly honest.

Several months later, he quarreled with one of the university proctors over an infraction of discipline the proctor claimed Stuck had committed. Hudson denied it, and he refused to apologize to the officer. For a time it appeared his stubbornness might be a bar to his continuing in the university. That night he walked alone in the mountains. He prayed, "God give me humility. Help me to overcome my pride and stubbornness." On his return he apologized.

There was a sorrow within him that he shared with no one. For three years he received no answers to the letters he wrote to his parents. Then came a scrawled note, "We cannot fully understand your actions. But you are our son, and you have our love, and our blessings on your ministry. We will keep you in our prayers."

In the spring of 1892, his student days at Sewanee were completed. He had been acclaimed the most brilliant of the theological students attending the university, and was told to prepare himself for ordination to the priesthood. The men with whom he had studied scattered to posts that would eventually lead many to the most honored positions in the Episcopal church. Hudson Stuck, a worn bag clutched in his hand, stepped aboard a train that crawled slowly south and west to Texas.

He had pledged ten years of his life to the needs of the Church. He was going to fulfill that pledge.

4

A cattle thief was hanged on the blistering hot afternoon Hudson arrived in Cuero, Texas. The crowds of the curious were still milling uncertainly around the gnarled oak when he walked by.

He rested for a moment in the shade of the hanging tree. He was tall and lean, and his beardless, boyish face was in direct contrast to the heavy beards of the roughly dressed men who pushed around him.

Suddenly John Bristol shouldered his way through the crowd. "Sorry I missed you, Hudson. Things were popping around here an hour ago."

"Who was it?"

Bristol lifted his shoulder indifferently. "Mendoza. Julio Mendoza. Had himself a little place about twenty miles out on the road over by my place in Victoria." He tugged at his beard thoughtfully. "They just grabbed him and strung him up. Weren't many questions asked." He took Hudson by the arm. "Let's get out of this mob."

Hudson removed Bristol's arm, at the same time saying, "You've forgotten. I've got a home to go to myself."

"But there's something—"

"Later."

Without another word to his friend, Hudson took his bag and walked down the dusty street to Grace Church. He rubbed his thin hand thoughtfully on the rough stucco. He placed his bag down in the rear of the darkened building, walked down the aisle under the graceful arches, then knelt before the altar and prayed. Afterward he picked up his bag and went back to the white-hot sunshine.

John Bristol was there again, holding the reins that led to two magnificent black horses. He tossed one set of reins to Hudson. "You walk away fast when a man's trying to give you a welcoming gift."

"Gift! John, you are wonderful to want to give me a present but I can't accept that horse. I don't need one. I'll be busy—"

Bristol backed off, refusing the proffered reins. "How do you expect to get around this country and see people? You take him. Used to be a race horse. Name's Blacksmith. Go ahead now."

Before Hudson could protest further, he galloped off. Suddenly he wheeled and came trotting back. "That herd of mine you saw two years ago," he said, "I've doubled it three times over. And land—I got it coming out of my ears! You could shoot a cannon in four directions and not hit a fence post. I'm spreading out, son. I'm getting my piece of Texas."

Then he turned and was off again. Hudson watched him disappear in a swirl of dust. Then, the bag banging against one knee, and the reins draped over his shoulder, he walked across the parched grass to the rectory. Blacksmith followed.

That night Hudson was unable to sleep. He rose before dawn, saddled Blacksmith and started down the dirt road toward Victoria. The sun came up, a white ball of fire. Twenty miles from Cuero he saw a crumbling adobe hut silhouetted against the early morning sky. He turned in through a sagging gate, trotting past a newly made grave. A young woman, a black scarf on her head, came to the doorway. Two small children clung to her skirt.

"What is it?" she demanded. "Why have you come now? Why do you not leave us alone?"

"Mrs. Mendoza," he answered, "I want to help." He took food from the saddlebags and carried it to the hut.

The following Sunday Hudson Stuck, not yet twenty-eight years old, was ordained an Episcopal minister. He could feel his heart pounding during the quiet ceremonies of ordination. He listened to the words of Bishop Johnson, and trembled as he felt the hands of the older man touched lightly to his head in the most solemn moments of the ceremony. He whispered his own prayer, "God give me the strength to persevere. Give me the courage to be a good minister."

Afterward he mounted the pulpit and faced nearly two hundred people who were crowded into the church for the unusual ceremony. He bowed slightly to the bishop sitting to one side. There was a faint creaking of wooden pews as the parishioners moved in anticipation of the first words of their pastor. The windows were wide open and stray bees droned in and out. Palm-leaf fans in the hands of elderly women moved languidly in the still air.

Hudson could feel his knees shaking. His hands gripped the sides of the pulpit so tightly that his knuckles were whitened.

"A minister," he said hesitantly, "a minister—" He paused and some of the women in the front pews smiled indulgently at his nervousness. "A minister is a channel between the people and God. I pray that I will be a worthy channel." All his nervousness was gone. The words came freely, easily. "The day I arrived in Cuero," he continued, "you helped murder a man."

The slouched figures in the pews straightened. The fans were stilled. There was one man who got up abruptly and walked angrily from the church. Others glared almost hostilely at the young minister who stood before them. But most of the parishioners listened intently. At the close of the services when he stood by the open door, most of the parishioners spoke to him warily, as though appraising this stranger in their midst. One florid-faced man thrust out his hand abruptly.

"Well, Reverend," he said, "can't say as anybody fell asleep during that tongue-lashing!"

The next morning Hudson was riding again, striking across the prairie like a lone fisherman putting out to sea. He stopped at the first ranch he encountered and introduced himself. After an astonished greeting, a bell was rung and the men came in from the fields. The ranchers gathered about the kitchen table with their families, listening attentively as the thin young man, chin out, head back, brought them the message of his ministry.

All day he rode, fanning out into the grasslands, toward Yoakum and Halletsville, seeking out the people, cultivating the friendship of scores who had been cut off from any religious activity since they first came to Texas.

The news of this young, earnest minister spread throughout the Cuero area. He was a new influence in a new land. Each Sunday growing numbers came to sit before him. They listened, wide-eyed and attentive, to the scholarly accents that recounted the biblical stories that had shaped the destiny of man.

Bishop Johnson, returning from his diocesan visitations, nodded his head in approval. He came riding by in the hot winds of summer, again in the fall when the first cool winds began to tug at the tall grassland. His third visit was late in winter. The bishop sat in the rectory warming his hands at an open fire. He looked over at Hudson who strode restlessly about the small room. "You've more energy packed into one small finger than I have in my entire body, Hudson. Can't you sit down, stare into the fire a bit, and be thankful for the peace of the night?"

Hudson grinned. "Sorry." He sat across from the bishop, but his fingers continued to drum nervously on the arm of the chair. "It appears I've got to be doing something always, keep occupied."

"Well," the bishop said dryly, "we'll take care of that. Next month you'll be moving over to Goliad, to St. Stephen's. They'll be plenty to keep you occupied."

So, after less than a year in Cuero, Hudson moved thirty miles away to Goliad. He thought that it was restlessness that had occasioned the transfer, but in speaking of the move, Bishop Johnson said, "It's been a long time since a man as brilliant as Stuck has been known here in Texas. He is going far in the Church."

At Goliad he drove himself relentlessly to fulfill his priestly duties. He rode Blacksmith daily, visiting ranch families, reviewing religious teaching that had long been neglected in the area.

In all things he was strict. Some said he was too strict, too withdrawn within himself, that he never learned to unbend and mix with his people.

But the criticism was stilled when, in 1894, he was summoned to become rector of St. Matthew's Cathedral in Dallas. Hudson left Goliad reluctantly. He had spent a few hours with John Bristol on the latter's ranch, reminiscing about the time, nine years before, when they had landed penniless and unknown at Indianola.

Dallas was the biggest city in Texas. It flaunted its 40,000 population like a badge, and the noise of the city was almost like a strident voice. After seven years in the "cow towns" even London-born Hudson was impressed. He picked his way cautiously through the big wagons, piled high with cotton, that lumbered toward the warehouses down by the Trinity River. Overhead were gaudy, flapping banners screaming in foot-high letters about the up-coming State Fair.

Horse-drawn wagons and long strings of mule teams crowded the dirt streets. To add to the confusion, squealing hogs were being driven through all the surging excitement toward the distant slaughterhouse.

If John Bristol were here, Hudson thought, he'd be a millionaire within the year. I must write to him.

He would have preferred a smaller parish and the quiet of open country, but had little choice. He worked relentlessly, was a respected voice in the church, but he was unhappy.

To Hudson his faults were overwhelming, and he secretly worried about his shortcomings, because he felt they were a bar to performing the full function of the priesthood. He knew he had the respect of his parishioners, but not their love. He tried to mingle with those about him, but with the exception of Bristol, he was unable to do so easily. When he visited Bristol, he spoke of them ruefully. "The housekeeper at Dallas," he said, "claims I'm untidy, nervous, unreasonable. Says I have about the shortest temper of any clergyman she ever served. If she thinks that, what do the parishioners think?"

"What you need," Bristol said, "is a wife."

"No," Hudson shook his head emphatically. He knew that he would never marry. He was plagued with an irritating cough and was sure that his time on earth would be shortened by it.

He had been at St. Matthew's only two years when he was named dean of the Cathedral. He was then thirty-three years old, and his salary was $3,000 a year, a large sum for that time.

Trying to throw off the depression that enveloped him, he started building a new cathedral, one destined to be the most important ecclesiastical structure in Dallas. He drove himself day and night, spurring on the building fund which ultimately reached one hundred thousand dollars. The cathedral, an imposing yellow brick structure, stood within a wide sweep of lawns and trees. At night, during the time when bricks and timbers and stained glass were being assembled, he walked rapidly around the lawns, looking with pride at the square walls taking shape. Inevitably his eyes were drawn from the cathedral to the stars, seeking perhaps to still the restlessness within him, by their very quietude.

When a storm ravaged Galveston, three hundred miles to the south, he hurried to the Gulf city and gathered together some of the children who had been orphaned in the disaster. He sheltered them in a new building called St. Matthew's Home for Children. At the same time he opened a military school, and to it each day came a stream of youngsters riding their horses, tethering them to wooden rails, then trooping solemnly inside for their daily instruction. Often, in the afternoons, astride his own horse, Hudson would lead a cavalcade of youngsters on wild gallops over the surrounding prairies.

If the weather was bad he gathered the boys in his study and read to them from the Bible, but mostly about the battles fought in those early days.

Characteristically, he formed a choir and was not content that it be merely good—it must be the best. He held rehearsal three times a week, a rigorous schedule that he was able to maintain because he had promised the restless youngsters a lengthy camping trip to the western mountains at the end of the school year.

He never forgot his penniless arrival in Texas. Word spread around Dallas that the Episcopal dean was a "soft touch," and tramps appeared nightly at the rectory, seeking a meal and a night's lodging. Often they walked away in the morning wearing one of Hudson's shirts.

Yet he was a stranger in a foreign land. After nearly eleven years in Texas, he was still stubbornly English. Unlike the thousands of Europeans who had migrated to the area, who became rapidly assimilated in the new and vigorous country, Hudson did not apply for citizenship, though the American flag flew over the cathedral and the school.

He resolved that, upon the completion of ten years of service with the church, he would return to England. There he intended to join the Episcopal Society of St. John the Evangelist, an order bound by the vows of poverty, chastity and obedience. When he received a letter from his older sister, Caroline, he knew he would never go back to England. His parents had been caught in a vicious winter storm while returning from a visit to her. On a lonely country road they had died quietly as the snow piled high above them.

Suddenly his life was jolted from its busy routine. In the spring of 1896 he received a hastily written letter from Bristol. "These eleven years of hiding in Texas weren't enough. I had word today that the London police have found out where I am. They're asking the United States government to have me sent back to England. I've got to run. Good-by, my friend. I'm going north to Alaska."

Hudson was stunned. Putting everything else aside, he hurried south to Victoria, but he was too late. Bristol had left without a trace. The sign over the corral was hanging dejectedly by one corner. Hudson removed the battered shingle and placed it in his saddlebag.

Back in Dallas he waited for one week, two, then for an entire month, and still no word came from his friend.

In the evening he walked rapidly about the lawns surrounding the cathedral. He was a ghostlike figure striding with long steps in the darkness, a restless creature of the wilds confined for a short time by the stiff brick buildings of a city. Far away he could see the cluster of lights marking the center of the city, but overhead were the lights that caught his eyes, the myriad of stars. He gazed fixedly on them, pondering the fate of his friend.

"Excuse me, sir."

Hudson stopped abruptly. He had almost walked into the thirteen-year-old boy standing in front of him. "Grafton! Grafton Burke! What is it? Anything wrong?"

"I couldn't sleep. I saw you walking. I thought maybe you would want me to—" Grafton looked apprehensively at the shadows beneath the trees. "It's dark. I thought you were scared."

"Come along. Walk with me."

In the darkness of the Texas night the lonely dean and the orphaned boy walked together.

Two years later, in 1898, when Hudson had completed six years of his ministry, an event occurred that was to swerve his footsteps sharply from the path that was, to all appearances, leading him to one of the high ecclesiastical posts in the Episcopal church. He had gone by train to Washington, D.C., to attend a church convention. That night, in the capital city, he walked into a meeting hall, and by chance moved to one of the side rooms where a tall, broad-faced clergyman had just begun to speak to a small gathering. Hudson stood in the doorway, undecided whether or not to listen.

"My name," the speaker said, "is Peter Trimble Rowe. I have the good fortune to be the first missionary bishop to the territory of Alaska. I've been up there for two years. I've come back to ask for help."

Hudson looked sharply at the speaker. Then he stepped inside the small room and sat down, a wave of excitement rolling over him.

"The Episcopal church had only three missions when I went up there in 1896," Bishop Rowe continued. "Two were for the Indians, a third for the Eskimos. It's a land bigger than Texas, almost one third the size of the United States. It's difficult to get to, and it's been almost entirely neglected by the Church. I ask for help, for volunteers to join with me in the ministry in Alaska."

He looked over his audience, and his eyes locked on Hudson's. Rowe was seven years older than Hudson, and physically much stronger. His face was ruddy with the glow of outdoor living. "No people on this earth," Rowe said quietly, as though he were speaking to Hudson alone, "need a champion more than the natives of Alaska. Gold seekers are beginning to swarm in on them. Without help they could be submerged in the movement of white people into the land. They could vanish without ever having heard the word of God."

Hudson could feel his heart pounding. Perhaps, he thought, perhaps this was what he had been waiting for. Abruptly he rose and walked away from the gathering. Over his shoulder he could see Bishop Rowe looking at him, disappointment written on his clear-cut features.

Hudson walked the darkened streets of Washington. "I can't," he raged to himself. "I can't go running off. It's not the missions I'm thinking about—it's John." All that night he kept hearing the plea of the Alaskan bishop.

He went back to St. Matthew's in Dallas, and from that

58

day on, it seemed that he heard word of Alaska at every turn. The big gold rush was on, and Texans were among the thousands of gold-crazed men who rushed north to the Klondike.

Whispers of gold waiting to be picked up in Alaska had drifted over the United States ever since Hudson had first landed in Texas in 1885. The interest sparked by the whispers had been sporadic. At times it glowed fiercely; at times it died to a faint flicker. Then, in the summer of 1897, the steamer *Portland* had arrived at the port of Seattle with "a ton of gold" torn from the Yukon Territory neighboring on Alaska. Suddenly the whispers became a shout. A kind of madness swept over the entire United States. Men of all types —and women, too—joined a tidal wave of adventurers seeking gold in the Yukon.

Hudson followed the excitement almost daily. Each night, poring over the map of Alaska, he joined the adventurers. Each night the realization of his obligations haunted him, and he pushed the map aside and concentrated on the ledger books marked "Building Fund, St. Matthew's Cathedral."

One day Grafton Burke, now a handsome, vigorous lad of sixteen, spoke to Hudson about wanting to become a doctor. The dean listened in silence. He studied the palms of his hands as though tracing the life course of the frank-eyed boy who had come to him when he was ten. Abruptly he stood up. "I'll get a letter off to Sewanee this very evening. If you are accepted, I'll take you there myself."

Grafton was accepted at the school. All during the long train ride back to Tennessee, Hudson's thoughts were on Alaska and John Bristol.

At Sewanee he walked again under the oaks, explored the mountain paths and the wilderness glens and the damp caves where he had spent so many happy hours. For a few days he knew an end to the restlessness that nagged at him. Perhaps he could find the peace he was seeking if he were to stay on at Sewanee as a teacher. But he knew better—there was work to be done in Texas.

When he returned to Dallas he tried to conceal the grief gnawing at him by working with an intensity that was frightening. He was filled with a driving sense of haste, as though the task assigned to him had to be finished quickly. He spent longer hours of preparation on his sermons. He preached in a clear voice and, with his mind darting back to student days at Sewanee, wove into his messages a deep appreciation of nature, of the forest and the mountains—outward signs of the hunger that was locked up within him.

Late in that year of 1901, at a church gathering in San Francisco, Hudson again listened to Bishop Rowe pleading for ministers to come help him in the mission fields of Alaska. Hudson went up and identified himself. "I wish to volunteer for mission work in Alaska," he said quietly. "I cannot come this year, for there is a building project which I must complete in Dallas. It would not be fair for me to go at the moment."

Before Bishop Rowe could reply, Hudson turned and walked away. He did not trust himself to speak further because of the tumult of excitement that was building up in him.

5

It is 3,100 miles by air from Dallas, Texas, to the sand bar where the Yukon River curves across the Arctic Circle in Alaska. It was three years before Hudson Stuck was able to make the journey.

He waited a full year after his return from the conference at San Francisco before he spoke to his superior, Bishop Juhan, of his desire to serve in the Alaska missions. The bishop listened quietly as Hudson listed the reasons why he should go. Finally, Bishop Juhan shook his gray head and said, "There is much to be done in Dallas."

When Hudson started to object, the bishop held up his hand. "My dear Hudson, missionary work in Texas is just as vital to the Church as it would be in Alaska."

That was the first of many objections. Responsible laymen of the diocese urged him to reconsider his decision. "There are plenty of other men who could go north to take care of those Indians and Eskimos in the territory," they said. "Who is going to take your place in Dallas?"

Hudson smiled wryly. "Who was at Dallas before I came?"

The opposition continued, and Hudson, writing to Bishop

Rowe, said that he would be forced to postpone his departure for another year.

Even Caroline wrote from England, protesting his plans to go to Alaska. He tossed the letter aside without answering it.

The second year slipped by and his obligations did not lessen. He had been appointed to the Board of Trustees at the University of the South, and had to visit there each year to meet with the trustees.

To Grafton Burke, who had almost finished his college work and was prepared to enter medical school, he spoke of the vexatious delays that prevented his departure for Alaska. The young man, striding by Hudson's side as they walked down Curlique Trail, spoke up vigorously. "If I were you, I would just pack my bag and leave. They've been holding you for two years. They'll keep you in Dallas until you are an old man."

Hudson smiled at Grafton's enthusiasm. "A clergyman doesn't turn aside from his responsibility," he said, "and he doesn't act without the permission of his superiors."

Late in the summer of 1904, when Hudson's patience had been tried almost to the breaking point, he received reluctant permission from the bishop to leave.

Hudson went back to his room, fighting the giddy waves of excitement that swept over him. He spread his empty bags about him and slowly and methodically began to pack his meager belongings. Into one bag went mountain-climbing gear he had been buying, piece by piece, ever since his first venture into the mountains with John Bristol. Some day he might use them!

There was a knock on the door and when Hudson opened it, the bishop was framed in the opening. He looked beyond Hudson to the bags spread about the room. "I wanted to tell you," the bishop said slowly, "a committee of laymen is call-

ing on you in the morning, asking again that you reconsider."
He held out his hand to Hudson. "You have been patient
long enough. I am not insisting that you talk to the committee. Good-by, my son."

At dawn Hudson prayed inside the darkened cathedral.
Then he went outside and stepped into a carriage. Only the
faint clatter of delivery wagons broke the early morning silence as he boarded the train.

He stood silent and unmoving on the train platform. Then
the whistle of the locomotive sounded mournfully, the train
started to move slowly ahead, and he knew there would be no
turning back. He was forty years old. From that day on, his
destiny would be with Alaska.

He stared through the grime-streaked window at the im-
mensity of Texas, flat and level. In the early morning hours
the land was dark brown where the plows had been busy.
There were bright pastures where clean-limbed horses paced
the train before wheeling away in discouragement.

Beyond San Antonio there was a creeping change in the
landscape. The countryside began to collapse into stunted
trees and sagebrush and desert. The brown waters of the Rio
Grande came into view. Across the wide, shallow river were
the bare hills of old Mexico.

The sun was going down as the train slipped through the
narrow canyon binding the Pecos River. All about, fading
into the coming night, Hudson could see an unlimited expanse of rough earth, deeply eroded dry rivers, low sand hills,
rock and brush.

That night he slept fitfully, frequently drawing up the
shade by his berth to look at stars that slipped between the
dark clouds overhead. El Paso was rumbling noise at mid-
night, then Texas was gone, and nearly all of New Mexico
while he slept uneasily.

The next day he counted the miles across the deserts of Arizona. When night came again he walked a wooden platform while the train was being serviced, looking across the Colorado River to storied California.

At noon of the next day he was in Los Angeles, and the first part of his long journey to Alaska was completed.

There Hudson rested for a day, then went on to Santa Monica. He walked along the beach, unmindful of the waves that came rolling in, until his shoes were white-rimmed with salt. He kept looking to the brown hills that ringed Santa Monica Bay. Alaska was to the north, and he was impatient to be on his way.

The next morning he was on the train again. The steam locomotive toiled over the mountains, finally gaining the long, fertile San Joaquin Valley that rested like the palm of an outstretched hand through the center of California. They climbed up through northern California, into the mountains of Oregon, then burst across the Columbia River in the flat green lands that hugged the shores of Puget Sound. The broad white face of Mount Rainier was on the right, and, far across the Sound, like an immense backdrop walling off the sea, the Olympic range of mountains.

The train burrowed under a tunnel, slipped out into dreary rain, then came shaking and throbbing to rest at the station in Seattle.

Hudson swung down the train steps, and at once he was caught up in the excitement of Seattle, the gateway to Alaska.

The northern city, still 1,400 miles removed from the gold strikes, was different from any that he had ever seen. It was thrown up on seven hills, the buildings and homes stacked in disarray under the black-clouded sky. The city was squeezed tightly by Puget Sound on one side, and vast Lake Washington on the other. It was crowded with noise, the shouts of ex-

cited men, the straining blast of ship whistles, and the cease-
less clop-clop of horse drays rattling over the cobblestones.
The drays were bursting with goods destined for ships waiting to sail north to Alaska.

The waterfront impinged on the heart of the city, so close
that ships seemed part of the business district. They were tied
to long wooden pier sheds, and their booms swung in and out
as cargo was lifted high and disappeared into the holds.

Weaving in and out of the horse carts and the puffing loco-
motives were hurrying men, most of them roughly garbed,
some of them with packs on their backs. There was a clatter
of iron and steel as a pack slipped and frying pans and cooking pots rolled on the cobblestones.

Hudson followed the stream of human traffic downhill to
the waterfront. About each ship there was an air of impor-
tance, as though it had shared in a history-making event, and
was still involved in feats that would be talked about for a
hundred years to come.

Rain was falling gently the next morning when he left the
hotel and walked down the hill toward the waterfront and
Pier 34 where the steamer *Iris* waited. A crudely painted sign,
saying the sailing would be delayed for six days, was posted
near the ship.

Dejectedly Hudson walked back to the hotel, following the
carriage loaded with his luggage. Suddenly the rain stopped,
the clouds pulled back and, there not more than fifty miles
away, was Mount Rainier. A mantle of snow draped the cone
that soared 14,408 feet into the air.

Two days later Hudson was high on the side of the mountain. He followed a rude trail that twisted through the thick
covering of pine and fir. Hour after hour he swung along,
until suddenly the trail broke through the last of the trees,
and the naked, snow-slashed cone towered directly above him.

The trail disappeared, vanishing into the bare rock above the timber line. He paused for a moment, looking west to the jagged blue welt of water that marked Puget Sound, and beyond the white wall of mountains that marked the Olympic Peninsula. Then he started to climb higher, slowly, methodically, conserving his strength. He was a solitary ant in a sea of gray rock and crusted snow.

He was blessed with that innate skill that comes to only a few men who look upon heights as a challenge. He knew instinctively how much weight to trust to an innocent-appearing outcropping of rock. He knew just how much courage to apply in a swing over open space to an adjoining ledge.

He knew that it was dangerous to be alone on the mountain. A slight injury to his hands, his wrists, his ankles or feet could have been magnified quickly into disaster. He had talked to others who had made the climb; he knew the hours that would be required even if all went well. He knew of the unpredictables, the sudden storms that rolled in from the Pacific, snagging like hooked sea monsters on the snow cone of Rainier; he knew of the danger of snow slides, the treachery of ice bridges.

He knew of all the dangers. He did not ignore them. He accepted them, and he continued to climb.

He prayed, not out of fear, nor for help, but simply as an act of exultation. And when he stood in the pool of deep snow that marked the crown, he prayed in thanksgiving.

He looked out over the world, to the north, to Alaska. Then he started back down the mountain.

When Hudson Stuck came close to the Alaska Territory, in the summer of 1904, the land was just beginning to catch its breath after seven years of near-madness.

When the first flush of success was gone from the Yukon

strikes, those who had failed to find gold slipped down the Yukon River into neighboring Alaska. They found gold on the beaches of Nome in 1899 and 1900. Then, sweeping back in a returning wave, the gold seekers backtracked into the interior of Alaska. They found gold in Fairbanks in 1902. From there again, like wild surges of a tidal wave, the hunters slopped over into the most remote regions of Alaska, seeking elusive fortune.

Most of the men who descended upon Alaska were hungry for fortunes they intended to carry away to distant lands. Only a few, like Hudson Stuck, intended to dedicate their lives to the new country; only a few, like Hudson, were to make the territory a better place for their coming.

He walked onto the wet, slippery deck of the *Iris,* his mind going back to the time, nearly twenty years before, when he had sailed from England to Texas. Then he had been a wide-eyed youth of twenty-one. Now, he reflected grimly, he was an old man of forty. He knew that the roughly dressed passengers were staring at him. He shrugged his shoulders. He wore neatly pressed trousers and a tight-fitting corduroy sport coat. Vaguely he remembered that the bishop, in one of his letters, had recommended suitable traveling attire. Hudson, who hated the feel of the rough canvas material of the coats and trousers shown him in the outfitting stores, had decided to ignore the bishop's suggestions.

"If you'll excuse me, sir."

A small man with a fat sleeping bag perched precariously on his back edged past Hudson. Tied to the sleeping bag were a pick and shovel, steel pan and heavy boots. Hudson followed him down the narrow deck space that led between the staterooms on one side and the open rail on the other. The little man hesitated, looking at the porcelain numbers identifying each stateroom. He pivoted about, reached for the door handle, and the pack started to slide.

"Be careful, man," Hudson called, at the same time leaping forward.

The sliding weight threw the little man off balance and the bag hit the slick wooden rail, teetered, then fell over the side, dropping twenty feet into the dark green water. The loser vaulted to the rail, ready to leap after his lost articles. Hudson held him back.

"It's too late. They're gone." Below them a few stray bubbles marked the place where the bedroll had disappeared.

"Lemme go! I'll get them!"

"There's forty feet of water. It's impossible!"

"I've got to! Everything I own is in that bedroll!"

Hudson dragged him away from the rail. "Be sensible, man." In his impatience with the other's obstinacy, he had used a harsh tone, and was instantly ashamed of himself. Big tears welled in the eyes of the little man. Hudson opened the door of the stateroom to which he had been assigned, and brought the man inside. "Sit down," he said gently. "Tell me about it."

When Hudson's visitor left ten minutes later he was blowing his nose vigorously, wielding a huge red handkerchief in his left hand. His right hand was busy stuffing into his hip pocket a thin roll of bills Hudson had forced him to accept.

Hudson was standing at the rail when the steamer whistle bleated with an earsplitting roar. Big hawsers were freed from massive iron bits on the wharf and plopped unceremoniously into the oily waters, from which they were drawn up to the flat wooden deck of the Alaska-bound steamer.

The gangplank was withdrawn in a sudden angry clatter of steam winches, and slowly, slowly the ship eased away from its ties to Seattle. A tightly packed crowd of friends and relatives screamed farewell to those lining the steamer rails.

For a fleeting moment Hudson Stuck wished there were someone on the dock to whom he could wave farewell, or someone aboard the ship to whom he could speak of the excitement of departure. He wanted to shout with the joy within him. He wondered fleetingly how John Bristol must have felt, years before, when he had made the same departure. The buildings and homes on the sides of Seattle's hills started to grow smaller as the ship eased into Elliott Bay. Hudson scanned the blank windows. He was lonely.

Yet there was no unbending. He kept his lips straight, his eyes unblinking. A passenger, looking at him, muttered, "Cold fish," and turned away.

Hudson saw the movement and read the words on the man's lips. Inwardly he winced. He was a prisoner in a cold shell of reserve, and knew no way to escape. He was unable to speak, but he let his mind expand with the hundreds of new impressions that were being forced upon it as the ship started north to Alaska.

A thousand mountainous, wooded islands were tossed in a confused tangle, tightly pressed to form the Inside Passage to Alaska. Hudson knew this twisting waterway had once been a valley between an interminable range of mountains. A mighty earthquake had torn at the land, and the sea had rushed in, and only the tips of mountains remained.

He was on fire with excitement, yet he kept reminding himself that he was not a gold miner going north in search of adventure; he was not a tourist traveling in order to delight his senses; he was an Episcopal minister on a mission for God.

The ship turned into the Strait of Juan de Fuca, and a solitary ray of sunshine burst through the rain to light a path through a new world, a vast commingling of water and mountains and trees.

It was early afternoon. Hudson shivered in the raw wind that flowed over the stern of the rumbling ship, but he would not go to his stateroom. His eyes followed the double-pronged wake streaming behind. It was as though he had suffered from a great thirst, and the green islands were a cool drink. The rain stopped, and dark, swollen clouds hung motionless in the sky like soiled cotton balls. He quieted the excitement that pounded within him. "God," he prayed, "let me not forget my mission. Let me be a good servant."

For four days the ship twisted through the Inside Passage, at times seeming almost to push a way physically through the close-pressing islands. As far as the eye could see there were mountains, tree-covered except at the summits where purple rocks showed. Hudson left the ship's rail only to eat and sleep. He was in love with Alaska.

Lofty mountains with black rock walls carried on their shoulders, like capes, immense fields of snow and ice. At the foot of the mountains were small icebergs, skidding down to the sea, then tipping gently in the still waters. When the ship's wake spanned out to jostle the bergs, they heaved mightily, and frothy bubbles formed in the blue waters.

The ship crept close to the white, crumbling face of glaciers, whistle blowing defiantly. Massive chunks of ice shuddered under the impact of the sound waves, broke away from the main flow and fell ponderously into the sea.

Alaska, for Hudson, was a physical impact. He felt he could taste the whitecaps on the wind-whipped water. In his mind he could almost see himself climbing each white-tipped mountain. Each was a challenge. His eyes were lifted always upward, searching the thin craggy points outlined against the sky.

At the end of the fourth day the ship skirted the blunt end of Douglas Island, slipped down the funnel of Gastineau Channel, and put in hastily at Juneau to discharge freight for the gold mills that could be heard pounding in the distance. The passengers were allowed to get off briefly, and Hudson walked along the one street that hugged the waterfront, a street completely dominated by an overwhelming shoulder of mountain that loomed directly overhead.

He walked past small stores and scores of saloons from which poured the tinkling rhythm of pianos and the hoarse cries of drunken men. The sidewalks were of wood, and a few of the streets were made of thick wooden planks, but most were bare and ankle deep in mud. Rain pelted the town unmercifully. He forgot time, and the scheduled sailing of the steamer, trudging steadily forward between the cleft of two mountains that squeezed into the town. Within fifteen minutes he was cut off utterly from the world, striding along a rough trail that bordered a rushing creek. The mountains drew him closer, almost with a magnetic pull.

Then, remembering the ship, he turned back. He recalled that he was to have sought out Dr. Campbell, an Episcopal cleric and doctor who had established a small mission in the mining town of Douglas, on the island directly across the Gastineau Channel. But when he attempted to hire a rowboat to go across, the imperious whistle from his own ship sounded, and he was called back to continue the journey north into the distant heart of Alaska.

6

The twelve-hundred-mile journey from Seattle through the Inside Passage ended abruptly when the steamer edged up Lynn Canal, and came to a halt before a sheer rock wall more than a mile high. The town of Skagway, harassed by rain, emboldened by a reputation given it by notorious gamblers, was already threatened by the ebbing gold tide that was beginning to ignore it. The town provided Hudson with his first contact with those who were to hinder him most—the gold seekers of Alaska.

He was trodding the wet wooden sidewalks when outside one of the numerous saloons he saw a miner kicking viciously at a dog tied to a post.

"Stop it," Hudson said quietly.

"Mind your business, mister. This is my dog. I'll do anything—"

Hudson didn't hit the miner. He shoved him on the shoulder, but it was a hard, purposeful shove, and the miner toppled off the wooden sidewalk, flat on his back in the muddy street. Then Hudson turned his back on the man, and untied the dog.

"Watch it, fellow!"

Hudson swung about. He saw the miner coming, his fist cocked. He thought of Bishop Rowe's reaction to his new missionary's engaging in a common street brawl. He regretted it, but he did not flinch. The miner came at him, gathering strength for the eventual swing. At that moment the dog dashed forward and sank its teeth into the miner's calf. There was a wild screaming, a chorus of angry yelps, human and dog, and men poured from the saloons to see the cause of the excitement. Hudson slipped away. There was no point, he reasoned, in making things too difficult for Bishop Rowe.

He walked along the railroad tracks that paced down the center of the main street, found the waiting cars of the White Pass and Yukon Railroad, and slipped aboard. He found an old copy of a Seattle newspaper, and was still reading it when the train whistle blared, and the wheels started to churn along the narrow-gauge tracks that led up a green gully away from Skagway.

The White Pass and Yukon Railroad stretches for one hundred and ten miles from Skagway into Whitehorse. It took ten hours for the train to climb the sheer rock wall of the mountains hemming in the Alaskan city, then to skirt breathlessly along the shores of Lake Bennett before racing down a long slope to Whitehorse in Yukon Territory. It was a comfortable ride through a cold mountain paradise. Six years before, when there was no railroad, the gold seekers had toiled for two weeks to cover the same route on foot.

Lucky for me, Hudson thought, the trip is a short one. I've less chance to disgrace the bishop.

At Whitehorse, he again waded through mud as he transferred from the railroad to the *Susie,* a small stern-wheel vessel that would navigate on the Yukon River. There was an

74

impatient tooting of whistles, then the *Susie* pushed out into the yellow stream.

The Yukon River is 1,800 miles long. It sweeps in a vast lariat loop from Whitehorse, in Canada's Yukon Territory, across the entire width of Alaska, then dumps its muddy waters into the impassive Bering Sea. When Hudson Stuck went to Alaska in 1904 it was the main artery of travel for the territory. For sixteen years it was to be used by him almost as an instrument, while he floated over its waters in the summers, and traveled its ice-slick surface in the winters, carrying the message of his church to the most remote sections of the land.

But on that first venture he knew only impatience. The downstream journey was comparatively swift, but the distances were interminable, and it seemed the trip would never end. He lost count of the number of times the tiny steamer slipped in close to the shore, tied up at the bank, and took aboard a towering deckload of wood to feed the hungry fires in the engine room. The land was flat, monotonous—and endless. At a few places there were signs of human habitation, but for the most part, the travelers aboard the *Susie* could have been penetrating the heart of Africa.

In those summer months the sun was uncomfortably hot, and out of the bordering swamplands emerged the hordes of mosquitoes that ruled the entire Yukon Basin with rapier, blood-sucking thrusts.

But the excitement that gripped Hudson as he edged closer and closer to the scene of his labors was sufficient to push into the background all the annoyances that never entirely disappeared—the loneliness, the heat, the mosquitoes.

The salmon were running in the river, big, death-haunted silvers that pushed relentlessly upward against the current, seeking a nameless creek where they would spawn and die.

The native Athabasca Indians, short, stolid, possessing none of the warlike qualities of the States Indians, were encamped along the Yukon, waging a private war against the incoming salmon.

They waited in canoes near the shore, nets poised at the end of ten-foot poles. They gazed stolidly into muddy waters, then sensing some movement beneath the surface, plunged the nets downward. Hudson watched as the nets emerged with the captured salmon, saw how the Indians flipped them through the air, then tumbled the fish onto the riverbank. The women beat them with heavy clubs, then cut huge slabs from the salmon. These they hung like red banners from slender poles to dry in the hot sun. Behind the fishermen were white canvas tents contrasting sharply with the thick green of young spruce and pine crowding down to the riverbank.

The *Susie* stopped near one of the fish camps to take on a load of wood. Hudson leaped ashore.

"Where you going, Reverend?" the skipper called down to him.

"To speak to these Indians."

"Don't waste your time. Ain't a decent one in the lot! And we'll be pulling out in thirty minutes! Mind that—we don't wait for nobody!"

Hudson nodded his understanding. He fought his way through the undergrowth. The rough bark of stunted pines, growing tightly together, impeded his progress. Mosquitoes droned in the millions and he slapped viciously at one that plunged its needle into his cheek. His shoes sank deep into the soft mucky bog. He remembered Bishop Rowe's word of warning about proper dress.

Then he burst into a clearing and came to the camp.

There were twelve people clustered in the clearing. Skinny dogs growled menacingly. The women were dressed in dirty castoff garments scrounged from the refuse heaps outside mining camps. The men were just as oddly dressed, though their garments were even dirtier than those of the women. A child, almost naked, clung fearfully to one of the women. There was no word in greeting, only hostility in their glances.

Hudson stepped forward, his hand outstretched. "My name is Stuck, Hudson Stuck. I am a minister, an Episcopal minister."

His words sounded flat and foolish in the wilderness. There was a grunted word in reply. Inside the tent Hudson glimpsed a woman bending anxiously over a child almost covered with an old fur. "Is the child sick?" he asked. "Is there anything I can do?" He stepped closer and bent down to enter the tent.

Suddenly one of the children outside the tent cried in fright. Two of the women moved forward protectively. One of the Indian men, a jagged scar running white beneath his jaw, grasped Hudson's shoulder and shoved him away.

"Go," he said.

Hudson tried to speak. The Indians facing him were tight lipped, dark eyes flashing. One of the dogs began to growl and inch forward, its teeth bared.

The thin, piercing recall whistle of the *Susie* sounded.

Hudson looked from the tent back over his shoulder to the boat. He made a gesture of farewell, trying to smile to show his friendly intentions, but the Indians continued to stare. Hudson ran from the clearing, stumbling through the thick undergrowth. The sharp limbs and needles of the spruce and pine tore at him. He tripped on an exposed root and fell into marshy ground. Suddenly a swarm of mosquitoes, so thick they seemed to flow like a current through the still air, descended upon him. He fought with desperation, but his face was stung in a score of places.

In his mind he heard again the words of the laymen who

had tried to persuade him to stay in Dallas, "There are men better suited than you to take care of those Alaskan Indians and Eskimos."

How right they were, Hudson thought as he approached the boat and started to climb the frail plank to the deck. He looked back at the Indian fish camp almost hidden in the tight cover of spruce. How right they were!

"Hey, Reverend," he heard a mocking voice call, "looks like them Indians weren't in a sociable mood!"

Hudson stood defiantly in the bow of the steamer, arms folded, his eyes locked on the low shore line that dropped by. He knew that the mud was thick on his trousers, that his coat sleeve was torn, and his cheeks puffed red with mosquito bites, but he would not go below. He would not admit to failure.

The rebuff he had suffered made him more determined than ever to succeed. In a few days, he thought, he would be at Fort Yukon, headquarters for the missionary effort of the Episcopal church throughout the entire Yukon River Basin. He would plunge in immediately and try to win the friendship of the natives. He would become one with them, think their thoughts, speak their language, live their very lives until he could become so united with them that the delivery of the message of religion he was bringing to them would be an easy one.

But again he was slated for disappointment. The steamer tied up to the crumbling bank at Circle, taking on wood for the last sixty-mile sprint along the widening river to Fort Yukon.

Circle had been a booming mining center just six years before, but the new gold strikes at Fairbanks had lured away its adventurers, and the once well-rooted community had the decaying look and smell of a ghost town, the inevitable aftermath of the rapacious advent, debauch and departure of the gold seekers.

Hudson walked up to the Episcopal church and hospital, and found a note from Bishop Rowe. "Plans have been changed. Please come overland by stage to Fairbanks, where I will meet you."

Bewildered by the sudden change of plans, Hudson took his bags and climbed aboard the stagecoach for the 162-mile journey down to Fairbanks. Night came early, and a stop was made at a roadhouse where he had his first experience with tough moose meat.

After dinner he walked out into the darkness. It was mid-September and the first touch of winter was in the air. He walked past a corral where dogs, chained to oil drums that served as shelters, growled throatily at him. Overhead the stars glittered brilliantly. He shivered involuntarily. "I've got to learn to live with the cold," he said. He walked briskly, but the path petered out quickly, and he began to stumble on the uneven hummocks of the surrounding tundra.

Regretfully he turned and headed for the yellow light marking the roadhouse. The men inside were grouped around two big oil drums, one stacked upon the other, in which a fire roared. He listened politely as a miner retold the discovery of gold down at Pedro Creek in the Fairbanks region: "This fellow, he shot himself a moose, and danged if there wasn't a gold nugget stuck in the cleft of his right fore-foot! Well, you know, that fellow he just turned his back on the dead moose, hungry as he was, and backtracked until he found the spot where the animal had jammed its foot in a creek bed and picked up the nugget! There she was—biggest strike in the interior!"

At dawn the coach was on its way again, and the jolting miles fell behind as it climbed the 3,880-foot altitude of Eagle

Summit, then dropped steadily downhill on the rough ride into Fairbanks, at that time the heart of the most uproarious gold strike in Alaska.

Bishop Rowe, red-faced, stocky, was waiting to greet him as he clambered stiffly down from the coach. "Sorry things got twisted a bit, Stuck," the bishop said bruskly. "Come along with me. You'll be staying at the hospital." He wheeled and started striding down the wooden sidewalk.

Hudson hurried to catch up with him. "When do I leave for Fort Yukon?"

"You don't. That's the change of plans I spoke about in my note. I've been called back to the States. You'll stay on at Fairbanks until I return."

Hudson saw the bishop off on the stage for Valdez the next morning. Then he looked around Fairbanks.

If there was a comfortable place to stay in Alaska in that winter of 1904-1905, Fairbanks would have been the place. It was the largest town in the territory. More than 10,000 people were jammed within the log cabins that dotted the flat area on the banks of the Chena Slough, seemingly dedicated to one purpose—to erase from their minds the distance from their homes in the States and the inconveniences they were forced to endure.

There was electricity in the log cabins, and telephones linked many of them. There was live steam carried in pipes far below ground, an ingenious manner of delivering heat to homes. There was a fire station with a gleaming red pumper ready to dash out to quench any threatening blaze.

Hudson walked past rows of log cabins. He saw the earth piled high around the foundations to ward off the bitter tongues of cold that would seek entrance. Inside some of the cabins he caught glimpses of good furniture and fine china and glassware. The people of Fairbanks were ignoring the frontier. They were trying desperately to live like the people of Dallas or New York or Chicago.

He saw four young Indian girls giggling outside the steam-touched window of a drugstore. He saw an Indian boy emerge from a tailoring shop, carrying a freshly pressed suit carefully wrapped in paper.

Hudson Stuck, missionary to the natives, felt cheated. He had turned his back on Dallas, only to find Dallas transported to the Yukon.

For economy, Hudson was given a room at the Episcopal Hospital. The doctor in charge, a hard-working physician who had voluntarily left a well-established practice in New York City in order to serve in Alaska, welcomed him.

"We'll do our best to make you comfortable, Mr. Stuck. If there is anything—"

"There is. I passed an Indian camp on the Yukon. There were some children, sick children. Could you get aid to them?"

The doctor looked at Hudson. "There are many sick Indian children. We simply do not have the time to—"

"Then make time."

The doctor looked at Hudson. His face reddened with anger. "Mr. Stuck, I have my job to do. You have yours. I can assure you I won't tell you how to run your ministry. Good day, sir." He stormed out of the room.

Hudson bit his lip in vexation. He had not meant to offend the hard-working doctor. "God," he prayed, "help me to curb my tongue."

In his room at the hospital he sat at a small desk and opened a dictionary compiled by the Reverend Robert Mac-Donald, covering the most common words in the complicated dialects of the Indians who dwelt in the Yukon Basin. Hudson stumbled over the words. Instead of becoming easier, they grew incredibly more difficult. Inside him he felt growing panic. What if he could not master the language of these people?

He thrust the book aside and went walking along the Chena Slough, trying to push aside the doubts that assailed him. The temperature was in the low thirties. He heard people talking about the coming of the first snows. The leaves had fallen from the birches that lined the swift-running, muddy waters of the Slough.

One day he heard of a man named Bristol who was working a claim out on Cripple Creek, ten miles from the town. Impulsively he hiked out into the open country, his heart pounding, hoping against hope that by some miracle he would encounter his friend. But the man he saw slouched over a gold pan, spinning the creek water vigorously, was not John Bristol. Without speaking, Hudson turned and walked back toward Fairbanks. The tundra was brittle with frost. The countless small lakes were covered with ice, looking like white scabs on the browned skin of the tundra. A cold wind flowed noiselessly down from the low hills to the north. The highest of the hills was only 2,000 feet into the air, but already it was flecked white with the first snow.

Soon the long winter closed in, and the sun became a rarity. Standing alone at the window of his hospital room, Hudson could see the streets gradually empty, as people retired to the warmth of their homes. When he opened the window, the soft whispering sound of sled runners on new snow, the excited barking of dogs put to work after a season of idleness, were the only sounds he heard.

And those sounds electrified him. He smote a fist into the palm of his hand. Then he pulled on his smartly cut overcoat, placed his fedora hat precisely on his head and stalked out into the newly fallen snow. He marched down the street, though his ears were stinging as the sagging temperature bit at them. Near the banks of the frozen Chena Slough was a decrepit cabin. Behind it was a high wooden fence. Hudson pounded on the door. When it flew open, he tipped his hat to the woman who appeared.

"I'm Hudson Stuck," he said evenly. "I'd like to buy a sled and a team of dogs."

7

"Thank heavens," Hudson muttered between gritted teeth, "thank heavens they turned away from the town."

He was hanging desperately to the rear of a basket sled, pulled at breakneck speed by six dogs that snapped and snarled and lunged forward in a vain attempt to escape the restraining harness. The lead dog seemed to be fleeing in terror from the five who came behind.

Mile after mile flew by, with the sled lurching and pivoting. Hudson held on grimly. His hat had long since blown away, and his long overcoat was unbuttoned, the tails flying in the wind.

"You! You, Jimmy!" he yelled at the lead dog. He swung the whip, and the thin coil swirled about and wrapped itself around his neck.

It's ridiculous, he thought to himself. There must be a better way. He hung on, and the sled whipped over frozen Steele Creek and went bounding down to Little Chena River.

Suddenly the lead dog slowed, came to a stop and sat down, his big red tongue showing against white fur as he panted contentedly. Hudson walked around the team and looked at the lead dog. "You, sir," he said bitterly, "are a fake. A hundred-dollar fake. You are not a leader. You are an escapee!" He cuffed the dog smartly. "On your feet! And head back to town!"

As though he understood, the dog, Jimmy, leaped to his feet, hesitated, then swung about. The chastened team trotted back to Fairbanks, turned down the main street and came to a halt before the door of the hospital.

From that day on, Hudson practiced daily with the team. Soon he was as proficient as any of the miners who came racing in from the creeks. He discarded his overcoat and bought a shabby, secondhand parka, complete with hood and gloves. He let his mustache grow, and he was pleasantly surprised to find that a beard cut the bite of the icy wind on his throat.

The people of Fairbanks no longer spoke of "that odd Englishman." They began to give him a grudging respect, though many were resentful of his reserve.

Hudson was never busier. He continued to assist in the church duties at Fairbanks, preaching to the white congregation, visiting the sick and bringing words of comfort to the dying. But for him all of this was temporary. His eyes always looked beyond the city to the vast stretches of silent tundra where the Indian tribes were waiting. His biggest worry was his failure to master the Indian dialects.

He visited at the town schoolhouse, listening politely as the teacher explained, "Discipline is really no problem with these youngsters." She looked over her shoulder to the white children seated around a roaring Yukon stove. "They're accustomed to being cooped up from October to April under close parental supervision." She leaned forward and whispered confidentially, "It makes them more subdued, more amenable to supervision. And," she added triumphantly, as though imparting vital information, "when the cold weather keeps them indoors so constantly, they learn to play together better."

Hudson nodded approval. But he could not help thinking of the Indian children he had seen in the fishing camp on the Yukon River, some in rags—and one dying.

As she walked to the door of the schoolhouse, the teacher helped Hudson with his parka and said, "We do have a problem with the youngsters who are here for their first winter. It takes them a month or more to realize the dangers of sub-zero weather, to realize how easy it is to have their lungs frostbitten."

Hudson made no reply. All his life it had been difficult for him to talk to women. But the teacher did not notice. When she held the door ajar for him, she said, almost as though talking to herself, "When the temperature reaches forty degrees below zero we don't mark the children absent if they don't come to school. And when it reaches fifty below, we just close the school. It's impossible to keep it warm."

Hudson touched his hand to his fur cap politely and left.

The next day the temperature dropped, not to forty below, but to sixty degrees below zero. Hudson suffered from the bitter weather that draped itself like a blanket over the immobile town. For a few moments he thought almost longingly of the hot, humid summer weather of Dallas. But he remembered that, with the coming of the spring and the return of Bishop Rowe, he would be on his way to Fort Yukon. The thought sustained him.

The population of the town swelled with every drop in temperature. As the creeks and the ground crust froze, and it became impossible to work the frozen gravel, the miners came in from the outlying creeks, a migration of lonely, bearded men drawn to the bright, twinkling lights of Fairbanks. To the horror of many of the churchgoers of the city, Hudson Stuck visited the saloons and the night clubs, his sharp eyes roving from face to face, always in search of his friend John Bristol.

One night he went to the Silver Slipper where the click-click of silver dollars being gambled almost drowned the shrill notes of the girl singer. The piano player, gaunt, with high cheekbones and long thin, nervous fingers, nodded a silent greeting to Hudson while he continued to play. When the number was concluded, he beckoned.

"No secret around town," he said above the uproar, "you're looking for another Englishman named Bristol, John Bristol."

"That is true. He was a friend of mine."

"Heard a couple fellows talking. Said they knew of a John Bristol. On Beaver Creek, at the foot of the White Mountains."

"How far away is that?" Hudson demanded.

"Forty, fifty miles." The piano player lifted his long fingers in warning. "Don't get excited, Reverend. The story I got your friend was dead." The piano player turned and began a new song.

But there was no stopping Hudson. At seven o'clock the next morning, while the town of Fairbanks was still locked in darkness, he spoke sharply to the lead dog, Jimmy the Fake, and started out on the trail, heading for Beaver Creek and the White Mountains.

He knew that he was violating every rule for survival in a harsh land, but the thought that he might find some trace of his friend urged him on. He should not have gone alone, he knew. He was ill prepared for disaster. There was every chance that he would become lost in the white wilderness, that his team might run away, that he might become injured, that a sudden drop in the temperature would leave him help-less and freezing on the trail.

Still he went on. At first the trail, even in the early morning darkness, was comparatively easy to follow, for the mail carrier had gone by the evening before on his regular run to Chatanika.

Hour after hour the dogs trotted forward steadily, Hudson running behind, occasionally leaping aboard the sled to rest. At other times, when the snow was heavy he ran ahead, breaking the trail for the panting dogs who followed.

A gray, uneasy light that passed for daylight had come at nine in the morning, and it was gone by one in the afternoon. Hudson stopped briefly for lunch, then pushed on again, apprehensive with the coming of the new, interminable night.

Suddenly he realized that he was lost. He wanted to stop the sled and gather the dogs around him for warmth while he tried to locate his position. But when he tried to halt the dogs, they fought away and continued to plunge forward. "Let them be," Hudson counseled himself. "They probably know more about where we're going than I do."

On the banks of a small stream that emptied into Beaver Creek, he could discern a huddle of buildings. The few cabins were dark and deserted. All except one. The yellow light of a kerosene lamp glowed dimly. A limp plume of smoke hung low over the chimney. Hudson knocked on the door. An Indian woman opened it and stared blankly at him.

He spoke to her in Indian language but the words were fumbling, uncertain, and she looked at him as though he were speaking gibberish. He could feel himself flush, and automatically he reverted to English, "My name," he said, then stopped abruptly. The woman stood back, motioning him to enter the cabin. Inside it was almost dark, the kerosene lamp casting weird shadows on the log walls that were chinked with thin strips of rags. Two Indian boys, one about fourteen, the other perhaps a year younger, were crouched by a low fire. Another boy was stretched on a pile of blankets, his eyes closed, his head turning restlessly from side to side. The older boy nodded, rose and came to Hudson.

"You are the doctor?" he asked.

Hudson shook his head. "No. What's wrong?"

"Everybody sick. Everybody die. All children die. Fifty die since two weeks. Richard and me," he gestured to the younger boy, "we only ones left. Soon we die, too."

"No. We'll get help. Take care of my dogs. There's food on the sled. You," Hudson said to the woman, "heat water. We bathe the boy." He tried to speak authoritatively, but he was frightened. He did not know what was wrong, but that one boy was close to death. "Tomorrow morning," he continued, "when the dogs are rested, you take the team back to Fairbanks and get help. I'll stay. What is your name?" he asked the older boy.

"Walter Harper. The woman, she my aunt. This boy, his name Richard. Richard Bristol."

Hudson stared at the dark-skinned boy sitting crouched by the fire. Richard Bristol. He walked toward him, then stopped. "Help me with the sick one," he said. "We'll try to make him comfortable."

All through the night Hudson sat by the sick boy, but his eyes were turned to Richard Bristol, folded in sleep by the fire. There were scores of questions storming his mind.

In the morning Walter Harper sped off with the team for

Fairbanks. Hudson stayed in the stricken Indian village. As a clergyman, he was not unfamiliar with death. But death in Dallas was clean, dignified, an end reached in a sea of white sheets and careful, hushed-voiced attendants. Here, in the stricken Indian village, death was not clean, it was not dignified, and it came in utter loneliness punctuated only by the violent pounding of the wind.

Before he pushed back the door of each cabin, Hudson prayed for strength and understanding. If those inside were dead he tried to compose the distorted limbs, and covered the worn faces with blankets. Then he knelt by the crude bunks and prayed.

If they were living, he tried awkwardly to tend to their needs, bringing water, lighting fires, offering them the small ration of food he had brought along on the sled.

"Help is coming," he said haltingly. "Help is coming." He repeated the words over and over again, trying to remember the Indian words from the native dictionary he had been studying so painfully. Then in a rush of English, speaking to himself, he said, "Someday soon we will build a hospital for the natives. We'll bring doctors to help them."

All that day he cleaned the cabins, tending to the sick, arranging for the burial of the dead.

Richard Bristol was with him always. The boy was quiet, speaking in calm, clipped sentences. Hudson asked no direct questions. He knew, almost before he was told, what he dreaded to hear. John Bristol was dead. From the boy he learned that Bristol was coming up a mine shaft dug laboriously into the frozen gravel, pulled aloft by a rope wrapped about a windlass. The rope had snapped, and he had plunged one hundred feet.

There were other sentences that the boy spoke, and Hudson

listened in a daze, shocked that his friend was gone forever. John had been in the Yukon Valley only a short time when he had married an Indian woman. He had found her sitting by the body of her husband, with her son clutching fearfully to her skirts. He had taken them to his cabin, and when spring came, he went with the two to Fairbanks where he married the woman, and gave Richard his name. She had been one of the first victims of the epidemic.

Late on the second day there was a chorus of yelping dogs, and three teams with laden sleds pulled into the stricken village. The doctor from the Episcopal Hospital nodded curtly at Hudson. There had never been a warm friendship between the two.

"These diphtheria epidemics break out every so often. I'll take over now, Reverend. Thanks."

In the morning Hudson started back to Fairbanks. Years before when he had left storm-stricken Galveston he had taken back with him to Dallas young Grafton Burke. This day, as he started on the hard-packed trail back to Fairbanks, he took with him Richard Bristol.

They spoke little on the return journey. The boy had come willingly, but with no enthusiasm. He appeared constantly on his guard, suspicious, as though he were not quite sure of the reasons behind Hudson's request that he come with him to Fairbanks.

Hudson handled the sled expertly, and the dogs, chastened by the stern mentor who used the whip without hesitation, responded with a fresh display of speed.

The two rested briefly in a shelter cabin, exchanging information with a mail carrier who was also there. The shack was a way station on the sled trail to the Tolovana River gold-mining district.

It was only a few minutes after they left the cabin and rushed on toward Fairbanks, that Hudson brought the dogs smartly across Glenn Creek. Suddenly the ice gave way under his feet and he found himself in water up to his hips.

The temperature was close to fifty degrees below zero. It was a proven fact that a man who had his feet frozen at that temperature would inevitably lose them.

The sled had pulled ahead to the opposite side. Horrified at the sudden turn of events, Hudson saw Richard scramble onto the sled and heard the thin shrill voice calling sharply to the dogs. They stopped; Hudson pulled himself free of the broken ice and scrambled awkwardly to the shore.

Richard leaped from the sled. He looked gravely at the sheath of ice that was already encompassing Hudson's legs.

"Need fire, quick," he said.

Hudson looked about helplessly.

"Back at cabin," Richard said. He seized Hudson's hand and started to pull him back across the ice of the creek.

"What about the dogs?"

The boy looked impassively at the man who towered above him. "Need fire, quick," he repeated.

He ran ahead, and Hudson shuffled behind, his ice-encased legs like two shrunken stilts. He heard the dogs yelping, and looking over his shoulder he could see that the team had swung about, bewildered, then had started trotting back toward the cabin. As the sled came abreast of him, Hudson threw himself awkwardly upon it, and was dragged, half on, half off, back to the cabin. Smoke was already beginning to drift upward from the chimney.

He lurched inside, experiencing a momentary fright as the Indian boy met him with a drawn kife. The blade dug deep into the ice-encrusted leggings. Richard tore away the coverings.

"Is good," he said matter-of-factly, "no water come through." He stepped back, cleaned the blade of the knife carefully and then crouched by the fire, looking intently into the roaring flames as though he had completely forgotten the incident.

Half an hour later they were on the trail again, Hudson breathing a prayer of thankfulness that his feet, now sheathed in blankets, had been spared. He tried to express his thanks to Richard, but the boy ignored him.

At the hospital he had a cot set up in his study. "You will stay here," he said to the boy.

The head nurse came into the room and saw the dark-skinned head in a nest of blankets. Richard's eyes were already closing in sleep.

"You can't do this, Reverend Stuck. We simply can't have Indians—"

"The boy stays."

The nurse retreated at the sharpness of his voice.

He met a polite refusal the next day when he tried to enter Richard in the Fairbanks school. "I learned that it was liquor sold by white traders that killed this boy's natural father," he said heatedly to the principal. "His mother died from disease that was brought to the village by white gold prospectors. What would you have me do with him—drown him in the Slough?"

The principal rose to his feet. "We have our customs here, Reverend Stuck, and we intend to abide by them. If you want to fight for the rights of these natives, that's your privilege."

Hudson was seething but he fought to restrain his anger. He bit his lips, and when he spoke his words were low and even. "As you say, it will be my privilege to fight for these people. Good day, sir."

He held out his hand to Richard, who stood quiet and impassive during the stormy scene. The two walked together into the bitter cold that hung heavily over Fairbanks.

8

Hudson waited impatiently as the cold weather retreated hesitantly from the town. In a letter to Grafton Burke, who was completing his medical studies at Columbia University, he said, "It is not easy to endure such a long apprenticeship. Were it not for the boy, Richard Bristol, who is living with me, I would be as far removed from the natives as if I were still in Texas. The only difference is the cold and the distance, but people seem to be able to forget both."

He spent much of his free time with Richard. He started him on a course of studies that had one purpose—the boy's eventual entrance into Sewanee. The preparation would be a long and difficult one. Richard was unable to read English.

"Is no difference," he said, shrugging his shoulders. "You no read Indian language. You no speak it. Me speak English."

"Well, then, sir, we'll both get on with our studies."

The gold creeks in the shallow hills surrounding Fairbanks were once more crowded with restless prospectors as the ice turned to slush and the slush to cold, clear, swiftly running water.

Then the summer came in a rush of bright green that

spread over the tundra. The days grew longer, and the sun shone with a startling intensity. Hudson waited through the gratifying heat waves. The inactivity was galling, but he thrust aside his feelings. Above all else he was rigidly obedient to the bishop's request.

He labored incessantly, trying to master the Indian language. After a particularly frustrating session he tossed aside the well-thumbed book and tried to find relaxation in reading the early Greek and Roman authors. He noticed, almost with envy, that Richard was making progress with English.

Not until late October did the travel-weary Bishop Rowe return to Fairbanks. With Hudson he wasted no formalities. He sat down on a chair in the latter's study and looked at him critically. "I'm placing you in charge of all the church work in the Yukon Valley, from Fort Yukon over to the Bering Sea and north to the Arctic coast. You should plan on visiting all of our people, starting next month. We've had a request for a mission to be established up on the Koyukuk River, near Alatna. I want you to look into that. You know how to handle a dog sled?"

Hudson nodded.

The bishop went on quickly as though the skill were to be taken for granted. "You've learned to speak the language?"

Hudson flushed. He bit his lip in vexation. "No, I haven't."

"Take the boy with you as an interpreter. You can't very well preach to these people if you don't have a way to communicate with them." Suddenly the bishop rose to his feet. His voice softened. He placed a hand on Hudson's shoulder. "I had letters from people in Fairbanks—about you. I tore them up. The natives need someone to fight for them. If you and I and the other members of the clergy can't do it, we may as well pack up and go home." Suddenly he was brusk again. "But I won't have you go out on the trail looking like a member of the English Parliament running for re-election. Come over to my room, and I'll fix you up with an outfit."

In November, 1905, when Hudson started out on the 2,200-mile visitation to his mission region he wore a pair of smoke-tanned moosehide breeches. They were a perfect windbreak, yet they allowed ventilation and were warm in the coldest weather. At the bishop's insistence, he wore Eskimo boots with the fur inside on the sole and outside on the upper portion. He wore a fur cap and a heavily hooded parka. His mustache was full, and his beard a luxuriant growth that hung like a black neckpiece from his chin. Strapped on the sled were his snowshoes, and with them the moccasins he would wear when he used the webbed snowshoes.

Six dogs, led by Jimmy the Fake, pulled the sled on which were piled 500 pounds of equipment, including a tent and stove, bedding, extra clothing and food.

Richard Bristol trotted alongside the heavily burdened vehicle, leaning his shoulder on the gee pole to steady the sled when the dogs raced too swiftly into a turn. Hudson shoved on the handles thrust out in the rear. He felt a warm glow of triumph. He was started on his mission career.

They pushed along, making barely two miles an hour with the heavy load. When they crossed the Chatanika River, which was plagued by soft ice and shallow pools of water, Hudson was annoyed to hear Richard call the dogs to a halt.

"What is it?" he demanded. "Why are we stopping?"

"Clean dogs' toes," Richard replied. He squatted in the snow beside Jimmy the Fake and lifted the dog's paw, carefully drying moisture between each toe.

"Why?" Manicuring a dog's foot was the last thing Hudson intended to do.

"No clean, form ice balls. Cripple dog. Have to shoot him."

Hudson stared, then he sat down beside Richard and lifted

99

the paw of the next dog. "All right, Richard, you be the trail boss."

From then on he relied on the boy's judgment. When the ice covering of the Chatanika spread smooth as a sheet of glass before them, he was impatient to urge the dogs forward onto the inviting speedway, but Richard shook his head.

"Over here," he said, "glare ice is better. Make faster time."

Hudson nodded.

It was cold, and they traveled in a vast cone of white, smoky silence. The man, the boy and the dogs were the only living things to be seen. The scrawny spruce and willow trees were rigid. The faint sigh of the sled runners on the snow was a continuous, comforting sound. Once or twice a dog would whimper, furred heads would turn and a faint cloud hovering over the animals, caused by their exhaling breath, would tremble and eddy. There were a few moments when Hudson thought they should have waited to join with other parties that would be going north on the trail. Then he saw Richard swinging confidently along, and his courage returned. Walter Harper joined them on the trail; the three were to make the entire journey.

Alaska is so vast that place names become blurred in incomprehensible miles. To one unfamiliar with the land, the names of towns and villages and cities are like pebbles scattered in a wide arc over the sea. Circle, Fort Yukon, Chandalar, Wiseman, Alatna, Kobuk, Kotzebue, Point Hope, Candle, Council, Nome, White Mountain, Ungalik, Kaltag, Koyukuk, Tanana, Nenana and Fairbanks—this was the sweep of the Episcopal mission territory the stubborn, determined Englishman was about to conquer.

Hudson Stuck was forty-two years old. His health was fair, but his strength was not great. The same journey had been made by other men, but they had been urged on by a craving for gold. Hudson was urged on by love of a people who did not know he was coming, who would not understand his words when he came, and who would, at first, be suspicious of his motives.

Yet he never hesitated. He was like an infant learning to walk. This journey into the forbidding land was his first faltering step.

At any time he could have turned his back on the hardships, the risks, the lack of intellectual companionship, and retreated honorably to a safe, secure, intellectually stimulating position in the Episcopal hierarchy in the States. But he kept going.

He didn't grow accustomed to hardship. The "wild beast" wind that slashed at him when he first pierced the Chandalar Gap was still a hated enemy when he made the cruel run through the canyons of the Koyukuk.

The heavily burdened sled tilted and overturned many times. He labored with Richard and Walter each time to unload the contents, right the sled and reload the tent and stove and food and clothing. He was exhausted when it happened early in the trip; his exhaustion continued and multiplied in the scores of times it happened afterward.

One night they came upon a wretched abandoned cabin, typical of the hundreds of lonely beacons that dotted the Alaskan landscape, symbol of some frustrated gold prospector who had burned high with hope, raised a hasty shelter, then passed on with the coming of the spring. It had no doors, no windows. The siding was full of holes, and nowhere could even Richard, much smaller than Hudson, stand upright. But it was shelter and not to be ignored.

While Richard fed the dogs, Hudson and Walter struggled with the canvas sled cover to make an outer door and used a blanket to fashion an inner door. They stopped up the worst of the holes with sacking. Then together they cut spruces for bedding.

Before they turned into their sleeping bags, Hudson sat with the two boys under the light of a guttering candle. "Open your schoolbooks," he said calmly to Richard. "We'll continue with your lessons." To Walter he handed a New Testament. "You will read the Gospel for the day."

Richard blinked his large brown eyes, but he stilled the protest that came automatically and began to read aloud the passage from *Treasure Island*.

The journey continued. When they were forced to camp in the open, they hung the tent by a ridgerope strung between two spruce trees. Richard took a snowshoe and scraped boughs and spread them inside the tent in a thick and generous layer.

The stove was set up within the tent, the fat pipe sticking upward through the opening. The fish for the dogs was cut up first, and cooked on the fire roaring within the stove. Then snow was melted for their own cooking purposes. While Richard busied himself preparing the meal, Hudson and Walter were outside, banking snow high about the tent to cut down the wind.

After they ate, Hudson insisted that he scrub clean the pots that had been used. Richard, always on the move, went outside and cut small spruce on which the dogs would lie during the night.

There was a short session with the textbooks and religious instruction, then the three weary travelers turned into their sleeping bags. Hudson reached out and snuffed the guttering candle. He uttered a prayer for their safety, and fell into an exhausted sleep.

They were on the trail one morning when the temperature began to drop fast. The mercury within the thermometer which Hudson carried reached seventy-two degrees below zero. Walter came to his side. "We find cabin quickly."

Hudson nodded. He exhaled heavily and expiration of his breath made a crackling sound. The dogs whimpered uneasily. He could feel the warmth oozing from his body and the cold creeping in. There was a loud pistollike report, and Hudson jumped, startled. Richard grinned. He pointed to a thin spruce tree beside the trail. "Tree freeze," he explained. "Split by cold."

"Too far back to last night's cabin," Walter said, hesitantly. He looked ahead. "Maybe another cabin around bend in trail."

They started forward again, their hopes quickening, then ebbing as they made each turn with still no shelter in sight.

The hours dragged by. Each time Hudson inhaled he felt a dull pain strike deep within his lungs. He felt a numbness in his hands and feet, and when he lifted his head and peered through frost-rimmed eyebrows at Walter, he saw the young boy looking at him anxiously. He shook his head reassuringly. He did not want Walter to know how close he was to giving up. He could feel his wits begin to wander. He wanted desperately to command that they stop, that they rest for a while curled up in the snow. He thought disjointedly of John Bristol, and Dallas, of his boyhood home in England.

But he stumbled frantically on, threshing his body with his arms, forcing his gait to the uttermost. He was afraid, almost terrified, as he felt death stealing in on him. Then he regained his composure, and while he continued to hobble awkwardly along the trail, he prayed. "God," he said almost conversationally, "I thank you for all the good things you have given to me. If it is Your will, let these two young boys live." Then he closed his eyes while he continued to stumble forward. He was sleepy.

There was a sudden cry from Richard. He pointed ahead to a weak plume of smoke that hovered uncertainly over a distant clump of trees. Even the dogs seemed to sense the nearness of shelter. They yelped excitedly and plunged forward with renewed vigor.

It was an Indian cabin, crowded with natives. Hudson stepped inside. A sickening stench assailed him. He was forced backward into the open air, and then leaned helplessly against the cabin, retching.

Then he forced himself to walk back into the crowded room. He looked at the dark, expectant faces turned toward him. "My friends," he said, trying to speak carefully in the native tongue, "we have come a long journey—"

He saw the puzzled look on their faces and knew that he was speaking badly. He beckoned Richard to his side. "Tell them," he said, "that we are grateful for shelter. Tell them that I bring a message."

The Indian boy repeated Hudson's words, and the dark-skinned faces nodded.

Hudson prayed silently, then started to talk. He was embarked on his mission.

He told them of the Christian faith and the Christian religion. He spoke to his attentive audience about the mysteries of the Incarnation, the Crucifixion, the Resurrection and the Ascension. Talking through the boyish voice of Richard, he told the natives of the laws of morality, the prohibition of murder, theft and falsehood. He spoke of a world in which good would triumph over evil.

He patiently pointed out to them the faults that must be corrected. He said that leaving elderly people to freeze on the trail was an inhuman and cruel act, one that must be stopped. The wanton disposal of sickly children could not be tolerated.

The genuine affection he had for the natives was shown in the halting sermon he delivered. They sensed his love and they responded gratefully, sharing their food and their shelter.

The next day the trio left the Indian village and started down a long canyon hemmed in on either side by towering walls of snow and ice. They struggled over mountain passes, then clutched desperately to the sled, slipping and sliding down the lower slopes. At times they traveled along trails that were hard and slick with usage, and the sled almost flew. But for the most part they made painfully slow progress.

Day after day, through December into January they continued the journey.

They left the valley of the Chandalar and hastened down the frozen mountains bordering the Koyukuk River.

It was in this region that Hudson first met Eskimos. He was charmed and taken by those people as by no others he had met previously.

"I believe," he said in a note that he scribbled hastily to Grafton Burke, "that if it were my lot to be born again as one of the natives of Alaska, I would choose these simple, cheerful Eskimo people. God has blessed them with a warmth that is denied other races."

The journey was never easy. There was never a day in which Hudson was not in acute discomfort, often in peril, many times despairing for his life.

He hated wind with a personal animosity because it was so brutal, so malicious. He ascribed to the wind a personality, looking upon it as something evil that lay in wait for his coming.

It was a savage, forbidding country that they traveled, desolate and uninhabited, a land of naked rock and bare wind-swept hillside, full of gloomy barren valleys. There were a few things that compensated for the bitter hardships he suffered. One was his first glimpse of the Arctic Ocean when he had been 1,000 miles on the journey from Fairbanks.

All day long he had thought about it. Finally he was standing by the ocean's edge, looking over the dim, gray expanse that stretched vast and vague in the dusk. Hudson let himself revel in the moment, thinking of himself as one with Balboa who had once stood and looked upon the Pacific as he now stood looking upon the Arctic. For him the frozen icy sweep of the Arctic held all the glories of a discovery. The jagged masses in the foreground and the boundless sweep of ice beyond held him in solemn silence.

But his exultation was short-lived. He spoke that night in a hut that was completely buried beneath the snow. Inside were crowded twenty Eskimos, men, women and children of all ages. They listened in smiling, polite attention as Hudson told them the Christ story. He warmed to their response and spoke until some of the younger children started to squirm from their mothers' arms.

An old man, crippled and bent almost double, rose to his feet and said to Hudson, "We have been visited by many white men. Some sought for gold on the beaches; others caught our fish in the streams; still others shot our caribou. What is it you seek from us?"

Hudson flushed. He knew then they had understood none of his eloquence. He had been carried away with the sound of his words. "We seek only to lead you and your people to God," he answered slowly.

The old man looked at him fixedly. Hudson could read the doubt in his eyes. He spoke to Richard and Walter, then turned and left the hut.

A short time later when he crawled into his sleeping bag he was so discouraged he was unable to sleep. He tried to pray but the words were halting and uncertain. "I seek only to lead them to you, God. But how?"

He spent the entire night tossing and turning, waiting for the dawn. Then he rose and sought out the old man. "We seek only to help you and your people. We will start a school and teach your children to read and to write."

The old man looked at him skeptically. "This would be better," he asked, "than making them good hunters, good fishermen?"

"Yes," Hudson said stubbornly. "They will speak for you when the laws are being made. They will protect you when others try to take what is yours—the game, the fish, the land on which you live."

The old man nodded. "When?" he asked.

"Next year. Others will come. I will send them."

Day after day, week after week, the three swept along the Seward Peninsula, stopping briefly at Nome, then turning hastily eastward. They plunged across the peninsula to Norton Bay, fighting their way through the mountain portage down to Kaltag, then welcoming the smooth expanse of the Yukon for the homeward rush along the river to Tanana, to Nenana and finally, Fairbanks.

On April 11, 1906 they ended the 2,200-mile journey.

9

Hudson reported on his journey to Bishop Rowe, who listened to him in silence, finally nodding approval. "Now you know what you're facing. You know what you need. Go down to the States and get them—money to build missions and hospitals, more ministers to help you, and doctors to staff the hospitals, teachers to teach in the native schools." He looked at his watch as though he were sending Hudson on a ten-minute errand. "I'll expect you back before the ice forms next fall."

Hudson made the jolting stage trip overland to Valdez, then took the steamer to Seattle and the train back to Texas. He stood again before his people and spoke to them of Alaska. He had been gone for nearly three years. Many of the faces he looked at were strange to him. He wondered if he had been forgotten entirely. In all the time he had been gone he had received only one donation from St. Matthew's, and that was from the Children's Home adjoining.

He spoke quietly of the missions, their need for help. "I ask those of you who are interested," he concluded, "to remain after the lecture."

Only four people stayed, and they were bursting with only one question, "What can you tell us about the chances for gold prospecting in Alaska? Why didn't you mention it this morning when you spoke in the cathedral?"

Hudson rose to his feet, biting his lips to restrain his annoyance. "If I had my way," he said coldly, "I would forbid entrance into Alaska of any white man except those pledged to help the natives."

There was shocked silence from the four men seated before him, then, mumbling excuses, they withdrew.

Hudson's appeal for help took him from Texas to Sewanee, to New York, Boston, Chicago, San Francisco and Seattle. He knew now the rebuff that Bishop Rowe had suffered years before in making his appeal for financial assistance for the Indians and Eskimos of the Yukon Basin.

In New York he met Grafton Burke who was just completing his medical studies at Columbia University. They walked across the city, boarding a creaking, jolting elevated train on Third Avenue, then sat almost in silence until they reached the comparative peace of Battery Park.

"It's not only the spiritual needs of the Indians that bother me," Hudson said as they paused under the trees and looked across the haze-shrouded harbor to the distant Statue of Liberty. "The coming of the white people has introduced a score of diseases those people never before encountered. It seems ridiculous, but measles, mumps and chicken pox are deadly to them. They die like flies when an epidemic hits. We've got to have medical assistance. We've got to start a hospital in the Yukon Basin."

Grafton listened, but there was no response, and when Hudson left him, his burden of sorrow was heavier. "No," he said to himself that night in his hotel room, "I couldn't ask him to come north. He's just starting his medical career. Why should he bury himself in the Yukon?"

He continued his lecture tour and his pleas for help, but the response was not generous. He began to long for Alaska, and was anxious to return even though he was going back almost empty-handed.

The day before he was to leave Seattle for the boat trip north to Skagway, he walked by the waterfront, listening to the lapping of the oily waters as they touched the worn pilings of the wharves. Beyond the stern of a rusty old freighter he saw an extremely ugly little launch, tied securely. A battered sign, hung before the wheelhouse, said the launch was for sale.

Hudson looked at the thirty-two-foot boat speculatively. What if he were to have transportation along the Yukon during the summer? What better way to get between the missions: a sled in winter, a launch in summer—it seemed a perfect combination.

He came closer. There was a boxy superstructure on the battered hull. An old man came on deck, scuffed tentatively on the grimy deck, spat reflectively into the water and then returned inside. Hudson stepped forward, threw a leg over the guard rail and leaped down to the launch.

"I beg your pardon, sir, what is the price you are asking for this boat?"

An hour later Hudson sent a telegram to Dallas and withdrew seven hundred dollars, half his personal account. Most of it went to pay for the battered boat, the *Pelican,* and for its transportation by steamer and train to Whitehorse in Yukon Territory.

He watched in doubtful pride the next morning as the *Pelican* was hoisted aboard the steamer. Then, grasping his bag, he walked up the gangplank to join the *Pelican* for the journey north to Alaska.

"Just a minute, sir."

He turned, startled at the sound of the familiar voice, even more startled at the sight of the tall young man who grinned a welcome to him.

"Grafton Burke! What are you doing in Seattle?"

"I'm on my way to Alaska, to open a hospital in the Yukon Basin. Or have you forgotten your invitation?"

Hudson was unable to speak. He grasped Grafton's arm and hurried him up the gangplank. Almost immediately the lines were cast off and the steamer pulled slowly away from the wharf. "Now, Grafton," he said, his eyes twinkling, "now you can explain. I was afraid to have you talk sooner for fear you'd change your mind." Without waiting for Grafton to speak, he continued hurriedly, "Now I've got something to show the bishop, something no money could buy—a doctor for our hospital!"

Ten days later the two were standing on the banks of the Yukon where it races past the town of Whitehorse. Hudson looked at the swift-flowing waters, then at the *Pelican* which was pulling erratically at the hawser that held it to the bank. "It should be the easiest journey I've ever made in Alaska. All we have to do is to sit quietly and let the current take us downstream."

He stepped aboard and Grafton followed. Hudson led his young friend about as though he were conducting a tour on an ocean liner. He pointed to a narrow well in the stern. "That's the engine—a four-cylinder gasoline engine is the way I believe one refers to it. You'll find the tanks are full. And those reserve tanks have an ample supply to take us to the Stewart River where we'll be able to purchase more. Do you mind, Grafton, taking over the engine controls? I believe you'll find a switch and wheel to spin before it starts. The man showed me, but I must confess I was too excited to pay much attention." He hesitated. "If you're quite sure everything is aboard, we'll get under way."

The hawser was cast off, the current seized the small vessel and the *Pelican* was under way. Standing in the wheelhouse, Hudson smiled in satisfaction. "Any time you're ready with the engine," he called loudly to Grafton in the rear. He grasped the spokes and spun the wheel. Immediately the little craft turned in a complete circle and started, stern first, down the Yukon. Hudson spun the wheel again, and the boat responded eagerly, this time bobbing sideways downstream. It straightened, drifted off to one side, then to the other. Fortunately the Yukon was wide, and the *Pelican* had ample room for maneuvering.

"Any time you're ready with the engine," he called again to Grafton. Behind him he could hear the heavy breathing of the young doctor as he fought the ancient engine, trying to make it come to life.

The *Pelican*, like an angry horse, charged with the full force of the current toward the riverbank. Hudson spun the wheel wildly, but the *Pelican* still rammed ahead. The bow buried itself into the soft mud and hung tight until the current pushed hard against the stern. Then the boat was carried once more into the center of the racing stream.

"We have several thousand miles to go," Hudson said aloud to himself. "I don't think we can survive at this rate." He started to call to Grafton again when suddenly there was an erratic burp of sound and the engine came to life. As soon as the worn propeller started to bite into the water, the wild maneuvering ended. The *Pelican*, its ancient engine throbbing, began to respond almost docilely to the nudging commands of Hudson at the wheel. Grafton Burke sat in the narrow well that surrounded the pounding machinery. He rubbed his grease-flecked fingers across his cheeks, rose wearily to his feet and walked up to the wheelhouse.

"Well, Captain," he said, grinning, "are there any other orders?"

Hudson shook his head, then broke into laughter. "I wish they could see you at Sewanee! What an entrance into Alaska!"

They stopped briefly at Fort Yukon where the great river makes a sharp bend for the sweeping run across Alaska. "It's the center of trapping activity," Hudson explained to Grafton, "an ideal place for the hospital we'll build."

"Does it get cold in winter?"

"The coldest in Alaska. Temperatures have been recorded at seventy-eight degrees below. But," he added hastily when he saw the look on Grafton's face, "the summers are just the opposite. It's been known to reach one hundred degrees."

In their brief stay at Fort Yukon, they drew up plans for the small log cabin hospital, to be called St. Stephen's. Then Hudson engaged some natives to do the construction. "We still have time to go down to Nulato, then up to the Koyukuk and the new mission at Allakaket. You'll be of greater service to the natives if you come along with me, rather than fretting over the way the hospital is being built."

He planned the trip carefully, but it came close to ending in disaster. When they were still more than a hundred miles from the mission at Allakaket, where they intended to leave the *Pelican* for the winter, they woke one morning to find that ice had formed all about the boat, and the river was white with small ice cakes bobbing menacingly about.

When they started forward the ice cakes converged as though they were alive, ramming with a grinding noise against the thin wooden hull of the boat.

"A few more like that," Hudson said quietly, "and we'll have no more boat." He pointed ahead to a small creek emptying into the Koyukuk River. "We'll tie up there and see if we can devise some sort of shield at the water line. Perhaps a string of birch poles, or we may even be able to flatten these tin cans we've been saving and make a kind of armor plate with them."

They edged the boat cautiously ashore, and there, in the midst of the wilderness, they met a gold prospector who had just completed a cabin and was getting ready to spend the winter at the spot.

The stranger pitched in to help them, delighted with his unexpected company. But every hour the temperature sagged lower. A smooth mirror of ice formed over the river. It grew colder and colder.

Hudson walked out on the ice. "Our boat trip is over," he said. "We'll pull the *Pelican* out. We can't leave her in the water. The ice would crush her and she would sink in the spring."

They rigged a crude windlass and then, hauling and heaving, they winched the four-ton boat slowly out of the water and up on the bank. They braced it against the winds that would sweep over the river, and covered it with canvas so that it looked like a gigantic butterfly in a cocoon.

Hudson borrowed a sled from the prospector, and they resolutely started the hundred-mile journey to the Allakaket mission. He looked at Grafton Burke approvingly. "It's just as well you've had such a hard initiation. Everything else will seem easy compared to your first few months in Alaska."

For a week they struggled overland, finally reaching the safety of the mission. But their advent was lost in a greater excitement. A white man had been found starving in the wilderness only fifteen miles from the mission, and the

Indians who had found him had brought him to the mission to die. He was a pitiful skeleton who crawled on his hands and knees from the sled to the mission door. He was Grafton Burke's first patient—and he lived!

Grafton worked at the mission until his own building would be completed, but Hudson was always on the move, seeking out his native charges who were scattered in sparse handfuls across the vast land.

Walter Harper was with him on many of his journeys, but his constant companion was Richard Bristol. They went out times beyond counting, following the whimpering dog team down the Yukon River to Nenana and Ruby and Nulato, or swinging north and west along the Chandalar over to Coldfoot and down the Middle Fork of the Koyukuk to the mission at Allakaket.

Just as often they would journey south and east to Eagle and Tanana Crossing, crossing and recrossing the land. Each mile was stamped with a purpose—to come closer to his people.

He was in charge of ten large missions and another two dozen smaller ones scattered along the trail. To the young men sent north to aid him in his labors, he gave a warm welcome, then abruptly turned to the task at hand as though he were outlining military maneuvers. To the women missionaries sent north he was at first cold and curt almost to the point of rudeness. But as he watched their work, and saw their devotion to the natives, he relented. He accepted them, then warmly recommended their continued use in the mission field.

But to nearly all of his fellow workers he was a strange person, to be addressed formally as "Archdeacon," a man who never displayed his inner emotions, a man who kept always about himself a visible cloak of reserve. Only to a very small number, men like Grafton Burke and the young missionary girl from California whom Burke married after a short time in the Yukon, did he unbend and make known his anxieties, his frustrations. And even with those few intimates he drew an invisible line beyond which they could not penetrate. Only in his prayers, in the solitude of his small room, did Hudson open his heart entirely. "God," he prayed, "help me in my ministry. Let me bring to these natives the knowledge of Your love. Help my weakness. Give me courage to persevere."

He was not blessed, as some missionaries were, with a calling to a populous land, where his converts could be measured in the tens of thousands. Hudson's audience was a mere handful scattered over the big shoulder of a continent. He was not cheered by any large wave of conversions. It was a grim, tough, uphill struggle. His congregations fluctuated as the fortunes of Alaska rose and fell.

The spiritual gains he made seemed at times to be wiped out by the terrible physical scourges that swept over his charges. In 1906, the year Hudson brought Grafton Burke north to start the hospital, almost the entire native population of the upper Kuskokwim Valley died of diphtheria.

What sustained him in a work that was fraught with discouragement was his love for the native children. "I look forward to returning to a mission," he wrote to a friend in Dallas, "to see the children come running, to have them press around, thrusting their little hands into one's own. It is a delight that compensates for much disappointment with the grownups."

When he became disheartened he did not allow others to become aware of it. They saw only a stubborn Englishman whose gaunt body never did adapt to the rigors of the land. Other men, in similar circumstances, would have developed, over the years, physical stamina to withstand the difficulties.

Hudson never did. Other men would have been able to shrug off the hardships. He faced up to the hardships, plunged forward to meet them, but never really accepted them. His mind was in full control of everything that went on about him; his body was traitor to the effort. He remained always a sensitive, well-bred Englishman.

In his third, fourth and fifth year in Alaska, his sled still overturned on the trail because he lacked the strength to fight it; his dogs still died, or ran off; he still became lost, and he still suffered when he was forced to sleep in freezing weather in the open.

He found it impossible to cast off the cloak of reserve with which he surrounded himself, and after a time he ceased trying. The only affection he permitted himself was toward the Indian boys who accompanied him on his journeys. Even to them he was, at times, an implacable taskmaster.

After ten or twelve hours on the trail he insisted that they huddle about the campfire or the stove in a cabin, ignoring the wind and the cold, while he prepared them for the distant time when they might be attending school in the States. Someday, he thought to himself, one of these boys may return to this land as a missioner to his own people.

His bulldog determination could not escape notice. Countering the love with which he was regarded by the natives was the outspoken hostility, the scornful derision of many of the white people in the area. They spoke of him bitterly as "that crazy Englishman."

Hudson could not permit himself to return their hatred, but he did admit to an intense loathing toward the white men who preyed upon the natives, likening the intruders to the wolves of the Seward Peninsula who sneaked into the herds of helpless reindeer and slaughtered them without reason.

He was sharp in his criticism of the vicious practice of "Americanizing" the natives for profit.

One day he strode into a trading post, his eyes flashing with anger, and confronted the burly, bearded giant who managed the post.

"You, sir," he said heatedly, "are a thief. Last week you paid Jimmy Thompson one hundred dollars for a black fox fur. You know the price is four hundred. I demand—"

"Hold your horses, Reverend. You're not demanding anything. Me and Jimmy agreed on the price—one hundred dollars and a case of whisky. It was fair and square."

"It was wrong and dishonest."

The trader dug his finger into his ear. "If you think so, whyn't you call the law?"

"You mock me." Hudson spun about and left the trading post. There was no law. There was no one to protect the Indians from those who made a game of robbing them.

He preached endlessly that selling liquor to the Indians was equivalent to murder. He saw starvation wipe out Indian families whose male hunters sold their furs to buy cheap whisky instead of meat. He knew from firsthand experience of the drunken Indians who froze to death on the trail.

Those who derided him passed from the scene, and Hudson remained, upright, unbending, a lonely figure who was a unique hunter, seeking Eskimos and Indians to summon them to Christianity.

In the long winter of his fifth year in Alaska, Hudson was ill and was confined for several months to his room in St. Stephen's Hospital in Fort Yukon. It was then he started the first of his five books, all of which were to become classics and valuable Alaskan reference works. He sat propped up in his iron bed, a board across his knees, and wrote the title in a firm, clear hand—*Ten Thousand Miles with a Dog Sled.*

When he recovered from his illness he plunged more vigorously than ever into his missionary work.

The natives were his entire life—until the raw, windy day when he first saw looming on the horizon the mighty bulk of Mount McKinley, the unconquerable, the tallest peak in North America. He gazed at it in reverent awe. "I would rather climb that mountain than own the richest gold mine in Alaska," he said fervently—and this marked still another facet in his life.

McKinley is a giant in a cluster of giants. Around its 20,300-foot peak swarm a succession of blizzards, raging like a celestial controversy. From time to time the storms subside, the clouds fall back and the mountain stands exposed.

On exceptionally clear days it is sometimes possible to glimpse the peak from Fairbanks, almost 100 miles to the northeast. Hudson, in one of his journeys, came much closer. He stood by the frozen shores of Lake Minchumina, and looked at the giant mountain.

"It is not a peak," he said later, "it is a region, a great soaring of the earth's crust. Its snow fields, its glaciers, its buttresses, its flanking spurs, its far-flung terraces of foothills and approaches are so enormous that they completely dominate the view."

But Hudson had work to do. He was a missionary. He looked once more to the huge white mass on the horizon, then turned and nodded to Richard Bristol. The boy shouted at the dogs, and they raced along the trail.

10

Hudson's mountain climbing equipment continued to gather dust in the small room in St. Stephen's Hospital, where he had his headquarters. As though to keep up a vain hope, he ordered from Hicks of London instruments that would be useful should he ever embark on the journey to the summit of McKinley. One of these, an aneroid barometer for measuring the height of an ascent, was his favorite. Packaged carefully against the cold and rough treatment, he carried it with him on sled journeys into mountainous country. Standing on an icy ridge, he practiced with the instrument, his numbed fingers adjusting the knob screws while he dreamed of the day when he might be duplicating the effort on McKinley.

Accurate scientific information would be necessary if he were ever to make the ascent. The claims of Dr. Frederick Cook to the ascent of Mount McKinley had already been clouded. In 1906, when Hudson had been in the country only two years, Dr. Cook had journeyed up the mountain and returned with the claim that he had reached the summit. For a time his claim was accepted without hesitation, although he had neglected to obtain scientific instrument readings and precise geographical descriptions in order to verify it.

A growing disbelief swirled about Cook's claim to have conquered McKinley. Veteran prospectors who had prowled about the lower base of the mountain near Kantishna were puzzled by Cook's descriptions which did not fit in with their own concepts. Later, as they compared notes, they became outspokenly skeptical.

One of the most vehement in decrying Cook's claim was Harry Karstens, a thirty-three-year-old prospector, mail carrier and guide in the Mount McKinley region. He was to play an important role in Hudson's mountain ventures.

Hudson was at Fort Yukon, in February, 1910, preparing to start on a sled trip to Nenana, when Walter Harper, now a young giant of eighteen, brought the news. "Four of them crazy prospectors down at Fairbanks, they bet they're going to climb McKinley, to show Dr. Cook was a liar."

Hudson shrugged his shoulders. "They've no experience in mountain climbing. It's a foolhardy attempt. They'll be fortunate if they don't get killed."

Late in April he was in Fairbanks to confer with Bishop Rowe when, from one of the saloons, an enormous cheer rent the still air. There was a volley of pistol shots, and the dogs chained in the huts around town began a wild chorus of yelping.

"What is it?" Hudson demanded.

Bishop Rowe cocked his eyebrows. "You mean you're a mountain climber and haven't heard the news?"

"What news?"

"Taylor, Anderson, McGonogill—they've climbed Mount McKinley. They've been celebrating for days."

Hudson felt a twisting pang of envy. The mountain had

been climbed again! But someday he would do it. He excused himself to the bishop and started to leave.

"You're going down to the saloon?" the bishop asked.

Hudson nodded.

"Well," the bishop said slowly, "I don't suppose there's much chance you'll get those three wild men to come up here—so, go ahead."

Hudson walked along the main street, past the fireplugs that were hidden within fat wooden boxes filled with sawdust. He walked determinedly to the saloon, shoved open the frosted door and strode in. A hush came over the murky room, then immediately the wild crying and screaming filled the place again.

"Come on in, Reverend! Come on in and listen how the boys did it! That Cook, he was a liar, a low-down, good-for-nothing liar! He never climbed that mountain! No, sir, here's the boys who did it—Taylor and Anderson and McGonogill —the best gol-darned prospectors and gold miners in Alaska!" It was Harry Karstens who yelled the greeting.

Hudson walked resolutely to the bar and looked beyond Karstens to the bleary-eyed trio standing with arms linked about each other in close comradeship.

"Tell me about it," he said quietly.

"Not at the bar, Reverend," the tall, muscular Karstens said. "Come on over to the table in the corner. They'll tell you everything."

The five huddled around the table, Hudson completely engrossed in the feat being recounted, oblivious to the noise and confusion about him.

"We left in the middle of February," Pete Anderson said. "Right down the Kantishna, then Moose Creek to the base of the mountain. We set up a base camp at the mouth of Cache Creek by the first of March."

123

"What we found out, Reverend," Bill Taylor interjected, "was that Muldrow Glacier is the only way in. You got to climb it if you want to get to the top."

"We spent the whole month of March crawling around that glacier," Charlie McGonogill interrupted. "Like a couple of crazy mountain goats that didn't know no better than not to go home. But we had plenty of grub, and nothing to do back on our claims till the ice went out, and besides—we'd bet a hatful that we could prove Cook was a liar."

"Go ahead," Hudson urged. "When did you reach the summit?"

"April 10th," Taylor said. "We started two in the morning —and we just didn't stop until we hit it. Dragged us up a fourteen-foot flagpole, too, and jammed it in right at the very top."

Hudson could feel his heart pounding in excitement. "There are twin peaks on McKinley," he said, trying to keep his voice level above the din of the shouting crowd in the saloon. "One is North Peak, the other South Peak. Did you climb them both—or which one?"

McGonogill scratched his beard. "To tell the truth, Reverend, I didn't go right to the very top—but Taylor and Anderson did. I watched them from about five hundred feet below. My feet were giving out. I couldn't climb another step."

"You," Hudson demanded of Bill Taylor, "was it the North or South Peak?"

"Well, Reverend," Taylor said hesitantly, "we had a reason for picking the peak we did; we wanted the fellows here in Fairbanks to be able to look out with spyglasses and see our flagpole. That's why we went to so much trouble to drag that crazy thing up with us."

"Answer my question," Hudson demanded, half rising from his chair, "was it the North or the South Peak?"

"The North, of course. We figured it could best be seen in Fairbanks."

Hudson sat back in his chair feeling suddenly very warm. He wiped his forehead with his handkerchief. "You know," he said evenly, "that the North Peak is 20,000 feet above sea level?"

Taylor nodded glumly.

"And the South Peak," Hudson continued, "is 20,300?"

"Ah, sure, Reverend, we know now. We could tell when we got up there, the other peak was higher. But we were just too danged beat to try again. Anyhow," McGonogill finished triumphantly, "we did what we set out to do—that there Dr. Frederick Cook is a liar. He didn't climb Mount McKinley ever!"

Hudson went out into the cold, biting air, breathing deeply. Mount McKinley was still unconquered. It was still waiting.

Hudson Stuck was always generous in his praise of the feat accomplished by the three prospectors from Fairbanks. They had accomplished, in one wild, almost foolhardy venture, what well-prepared expeditions had failed to do. They had survived on a bitter, brutal mountain that fifty years later would still be claiming victims on its side. But they had not reached the top. In mountain climbing the palm goes not to those who come close, but to those who reach the summit.

He hurried back to Bishop Rowe, bursting with a pent-up request that he be given permission to start planning an expedition to climb McKinley. But when he saw the older man bent almost double over a huge map of Alaska, carefully inking in the names of the widespread Episcopal mission posts, he hesitated.

"You see," the bishop said intently, as though he had never heard of Mount McKinley, "we should be thinking of opening a mission in the Kobuk country." He pushed his glasses back and wiped his forehead wearily. "Our native school at Nenana—we should have eighty pupils, not forty. And your hospital up at Fort Yukon—we've got to add on to it." He tossed the pen aside. "There's no end. No end."

Hudson's eyes roved over the map. There, deep in the heart of the territory, was the giant, the still unconquered Mount McKinley. He forced himself to listen to the bishop.

"For the school, we should be fighting harder to get the territory or the federal government to step in. The mission— that's our problem. We've got to raise money down in the States. I want you to plan on spending the next twelve months on a lecture tour. Get us help."

The fine words on the map spread on the table began to swim in blurred lines before Hudson. McKinley was disappearing. He would never climb the mountain. Forcing himself to look at the bishop, he said quietly, "Of course. I'll make plans to leave on the next stage for Valdez."

"Good. When you go through Sitka, try to see the new governor. We need all the help we can get with this school situation."

The boat that carried him south stopped at Sitka on rugged Baranof Island. At that time Sitka was the capital of Alaska. Hudson walked through the rain up the steep hill, past the crumbling reminders of the Russian era, to a plain wooden building. He stood on the porch and pulled smartly on the bell rope. The door was opened cautiously and Governor Wilbur E. Clark looked out.

Alaska's governors were appointed by the President of the United States. Clark had been a newspaper man, stationed in Washington, D.C., when President Taft had appointed him to his post. In the gold rush days he had mined for a short time in the territory and had made several trips later to the land as part of his newspaper work.

"Yes," he said. He was tired. For most of the day he had been working on his annual report to the President.

"I am Hudson Stuck, sir, Episcopal archdeacon of the Yukon."

"Delighted, Stuck," the governor said, thrusting out his hand. "I've heard of your work up there."

Hudson stepped inside and followed Clark into the small office from which he governed the entire territory of Alaska. "The Indians at Nenana need assistance. We want to double the capacity of their school. I've come to ask your help."

Clark looked at Hudson in surprise. "I know of the need. I'm just surprised you ask me about it. Those Indians don't mean a thing to me—I mean, you know as well as I do they're wards of the Department of the Interior in Washington. What can I do?"

"There is much you can do. The Indians are being neglected. There are 177 villages in the territory that do not have a school. We've built one at Nenana, but we need help to take care of more children."

"I've got my hands full trying to get schools for the white children," the Governor said irritably. "You can't expect me to be looking out after the needs of every Tom, Dick and Harry living under a willow tree in Alaska!"

Hudson fought the anger that flared within him. "You're the governor—not just of the white people, but of all the Alaskans."

Governor Clark suddenly bent over, pulled open a drawer from the desk and tossed a sheaf of papers before Hudson. "Look, Stuck," he said earnestly, "I know what you're up against, and I sympathize with you. But as far as schools for

the natives are concerned, I don't have the time for them."
He pounded the papers on the desk. "We're trying to open up
the coal lands, get a railroad built, change the mining laws,
protect the fisheries, get some navigation lights in these
waters, rewrite the civil laws."

He shook his head in discouragement and shoved the papers back into his desk. "You've got to be patient with me.
Things aren't going well with Alaska. The gold boom is over,
and we're trying to learn how to live like people down in the
States." He looked at Hudson almost appealingly. "I've only
been governor for ten months. You can't expect me to turn
the territory upside down in that time. Those Indians can
wait. The world's not going to end."

"For them it is," Hudson shot back. "Their game is being
driven away. The fish that they eat is disappearing. The children are dying in droves from the diseases carried to them by
the white men."

Governor Clark nodded wearily. "I'm writing a report to
the President. I'll put down some of the things you said. But
don't forget," he added hastily, "my first duty is to the white
people of this country. After all, the natives have the federal
government to look after them."

Hudson stood up. He stepped toward the door. "If every-
one waits, the problem will go away. Within a hundred years,
the Indians of Alaska will have disappeared."

Suddenly, he softened and held out his hand. "Forgive my
rudeness. I have abused your hospitality. But the natives are
dying. They need your help."

He turned and stepped out into the rain.

Hudson begrudged every day of the year he spent in the
United States, starting in May, 1910. He was forty-seven years
old, and intuitively he knew not many more years would be
left for him to continue his Alaskan work. He never spoke of

his health to anyone. Even Bishop Rowe, watching his herculean efforts in getting about his mission stations, took it for granted that the Englishman's thin, spare frame housed a constitution of steel. Hudson knew otherwise; he said nothing.

During the lecture tour he stuck doggedly and honestly to the exhausting schedule that had been planned for him. He rose early in the morning to catch trains, traveling long distances, stepping off in strange cities to be met by strangers. They conducted him to an endless succession of cold, drafty lecture halls, where seas of white faces looked up at him, listening intently.

Each night he slept in a strange bed, tossing restlessly, his thoughts going constantly to the Yukon and the work that remained to be done. When sleep eluded him, he got out of bed, and stood silent and unmoving, looking out over a city wrapped in darkness. Nashville and Boston, Philadelphia and Sacramento, Richmond and Los Angeles—in the middle of the night they were all the same to a lonely man who had allowed himself the luxury of only one personal desire, and that desire, he thought, was never to be fulfilled.

In Washington, he spoke to Department of Interior officials about the needs of the Indians. He was listened to respectfully, and copious notes were made of his suggestions for improvement, but always he detected a note of impatience on the part of his listeners. They were governing Alaska comfortably, he thought, from a distance of 5,000 miles. A voice directly from the Yukon Basin was an irritation that threatened the well-ordered ways of their administration.

In New York City, on one of his infrequent holidays, he walked endlessly through one of the large sporting goods stores, checking mountain climbing equipment and supplies, jotting down prices in a small notebook, giving to the few hours of recreation all the intense concentration of a child sampling Christmas toys.

In Boston he visited a small private school and made arrangements for the entrance of Richard Bristol. In the systematic program Hudson had planned, the boy, now seventeen years old, would attend school several years in the States, preparing for his entry into Sewanee. Hudson had spoken to Richard about this prior to his departure from Alaska. The boy had listened but said nothing.

The year finally dragged to an end, and it was fruitful mostly in the number of volunteers he had secured who would come north to work for the Episcopal missions. One of them was Roger Tatum, a twenty-year-old Tennessean, a student for the ministry at Sewanee, who volunteered to spend the summer in the Yukon missions.

Hudson had earned a fair financial return from his lectures also, but, as he remarked ruefully in a letter to Bishop Rowe, there was never enough money for missionary work. The need continually outstripped the donations.

In the spring of 1911 he was back at his post, overjoyed to be standing once again on the banks of the Yukon, surrounded by a welcoming throng of natives, the broad, darkskinned faces expressing genuine happiness at his return. Even Richard returned the warmth of Hudson's greeting, throwing his arms about the older man in one of the few demonstrations of affection that the tight-lipped youth ever permitted himself.

Hudson plunged immediately into his work, setting out almost at once in the aging *Pelican* for an inspection trip downriver. The launch, nearing the 20,000-mile mark of service on the Yukon, seemed to share the jubilation of the natives who greeted Hudson at every stop. The engine seemed to bang with a louder and more confident noise as it fought the endless battle against the Yukon current. Walter Harper chuckled as he called Hudson's attention to the surging power.

"Old boat," he said, "will go on forever."

The summer ended and the ice began to creep over the rivers. Hudson went back to St. Stephen's, to his room in the hospital and began to make his plans for winter journeys to the outlying missions.

Bishop Rowe appeared one night, unceremoniously tossed his hat at Richard and sat down abruptly at the table in Hudson's study. He stared across the kerosene lamp that separated them.

"How much money," he demanded, "would you need if you were to try to climb Mount McKinley? Have you thought of that?"

Hudson could feel his heart pounding. "Yes. Those prospectors from Fairbanks made the climb for $500. I couldn't take the chances they did. I couldn't risk the lives of those who would come with me." He paused to catch his breath. "I could do it, with four or five persons in the party, for $1,000."

There was a long silence and the bishop rose slowly from his chair. "I'm sorry, Hudson, I know what this means to you. But I can't in conscience release church funds for that kind of a venture." He walked a few steps on the rough wooden floor and turned about. "I can give you permission to leave your mission post for whatever time is needed. The rest would be up to you."

Hudson nodded. "I could not have accepted church money even if it had been offered. However, I will accept your permission to make the trip."

"Good. When will you make the climb?"

Hudson hesitated. There was so much to be done. Planning the expedition alone would be a major effort. "Next March. And, sir, may I plan on using the *Pelican* to carry supplies to the base camp?"

The bishop grinned. "If you think that old bucket will make the trip—of course."

11

It was in the fall of 1911 that Hudson received permission to attempt the mountain climb. In his quick, methodical manner his mind leaped ahead—the expedition would start in the spring of 1912, early in March when the trails would still be usable for the dog sleds that would be needed in approaching the mountain and hauling supplies to the base camp.

The preparations at the base camp, the establishment of relay camps, the final assault on the peak and the return to civilization would take three months. If all went well, the expedition should be back in Fairbanks by June, 1912.

Hudson had already selected his companions. Harry Karstens, the energetic mail carrier and guide, was his first choice. He possessed the knowledge, the strength and the skill that would be needed.

"Sure, Reverend, I'll go," Karstens said. "Tell the truth, I've been kicking myself I wasn't with those fellows who made the climb last year. I had the chance, but I thought they were crazy. Besides," Karstens continued confidently, "we're going to be the first to go all the way to the top."

The second member of the expedition was to be the tireless

Walter Harper. In the seven years they had been together, Hudson had learned to depend entirely on the young half-breed. He was with him constantly on the winter sled runs. In the summer he was engineer on the balky *Pelican,* possessed of an almost magical skill in keeping the wheezing engine throbbing at all times.

"You'll come with us on the trip, Walter?" Hudson asked.

Walter grinned and flexed his arms. "Mr. Stuck," he said, "I'm going to carry you to the top of the mountain."

Hudson shook his head. "If I thought that, I wouldn't go. I'd send you and Harry Karstens up alone."

"And Richard?"

Hudson nodded. "And Richard."

Richard Bristol would be the fourth member of the party. Hudson postponed Richard's departure for the States and his entrance into the private school in Massachusetts. "I want you to come, Richard," he told the unsmiling boy. "I want you to be with me when we stand on the top. We'll keep up your schoolwork just as we have been doing."

"I do whatever you say," the young man answered. He was nearly as tall as Walter Harper, broad shouldered and strong, but temperamentally he was very different. Looking at the young man for whom he had such a great affection, Hudson sometimes felt the boy was as much a stranger as when he first saw him crouched by the fire in the cabin on the White River, seven years ago.

Hudson waited impatiently for the return of Dr. Grafton Burke to St. Stephen's Hospital. He wanted to ask his advice about medical supplies that should be taken on the expedition. Burke had been called unexpectedly to the mission post near Kokrines. When he returned, he brought with him one of the missioners who had only recently joined the work in the Yukon Valley. The missioner, wrapped in blankets, tried to respond to Hudson's greeting. Then he closed his eyes as though inexpressibly exhausted.

Grafton beckoned to Hudson. "Tuberculosis. We'll have to get him back to the States. Immediately."

Hudson stood rigid, steeling himself against the blow. Three years of preparation had gone into the opening of the mission post near Kokrines. Overnight it was vacant. There was no time to bring a new volunteer up from the States. The vacancy had to be filled at once.

"Walter and Richard will take him to Circle on the *Pelican*. They can start at once. Richard can accompany him to the States to make sure of his safe arrival and get himself to school. When Walter returns with the *Pelican* he can take me downriver to the new mission. I'll make it my headquarters until we can get a replacement next spring."

There was no outward sign of disappointment. He wrote brief notes which Richard would deliver to Bishop Rowe and Harry Karstens in Fairbanks: "It will be necessary to postpone for one year our attempt to climb the mountain."

It was only when he was alone, the door shut behind him, that he fought his disappointment. The mighty bulk of McKinley was receding into the dark shadows of the room.

It was the loneliest winter Hudson had yet spent in Alaska. Richard was attending school in Massachusetts. To the long letters of advice and encouragement that Hudson wrote, there came back only short scrawled paragraphs of acknowledgment, a dutiful reporting of progress in difficult subjects, a strict accounting of the spending money that Hudson had allotted him. But there was no expression of regret for the distance that separated him from Hudson and Alaska.

Even Walter Harper was gone that winter, forced by a sudden epidemic at Fort Yukon to work endless hours with Dr. Burke in St. Stephen's Hospital.

He heard nothing from Harry Karstens. One traveler, passing by the small mission post, said that he had heard Karstens had gone prospecting on the North Fork of the Kuskokwim. The Mount McKinley expedition had been scattered to the four winds.

During that winter Hudson completed his first book, *Ten Thousand Miles with a Dog Sled*. Each night, on a rigid, unrelaxing schedule, he sat in the guttering light of a kerosene lamp, blowing on his fingers so they could uncurl in the cold and grasp the pencil. When each page was completed he placed it high on a wooden shelf, using as a paperweight a treasured can of peaches.

He never gave up his dream of the mountain climb. In February he drew up a list of equipment that would be needed the following year if the climb were to be made. He sent the letter to an outfitting store in New York, drawing on his personal funds in the States for payment.

He was at the mission station, alone save for his fifty parishioners who came and went in response to the movements of the game around that area, from November until late in May. The ice had gone out with a thundering roar, and the cold green water ran freely when the squat *Pelican* came racing on the current downstream. Hudson welcomed the bright-eyed, excited young man who leaped from the launch and scrambled up the bank, his hand outstretched.

"Roger Tatum!"

"Yes, sir, I'm your relief. Don't know when I'll ever get ordained if they keep sending me up from Sewanee."

"You'll be here just for the summer?"

"No, sir, until next March."

Hudson nodded. "Come on up to the cabin. We'll have lunch. What news do you bring of the world?"

"Belmore Browne is trying to climb McKinley for the third time. His party's been gone since February."

"There's been no word from them?" Hudson asked.

"None."

Belmore Browne was an artist and one of America's best known mountaineers. He possessed a tenacity of purpose equal to that of Hudson's. Conquering McKinley had become an obsession with him also.

They went into the cabin. Hudson opened the can of peaches he had been saving, poured them into two dishes and said solemnly, "To Belmore Browne and his group. God keep them safe and grant them success."

Afterward he took up the thick pile of manuscript papers, shook hands with Roger, then stepped aboard the *Pelican*. He was quiet. His thoughts were on Mount McKinley and the men who, at that very moment, might be fighting for their lives on the white slopes of the mountains.

Belmore Browne failed in his attempt to reach the summit. Near starvation forced the party to turn back, then a rumbling earthquake that ripped the glacier beneath their feet almost completed their destruction. Bruised and exhausted, they stumbled off the mountain. Mount McKinley was still unconquered.

There was a great deal of work waiting for Hudson when he returned to his headquarters at St. Stephen's Hospital in Fort Yukon. But he never forgot entirely his plans for climbing the mountain. At the native school in Nenana he established a supply base in a rear shed, adding to it as his journeys and money would allow. When the *Pelican* had finished its summer voyages, and there would still be a few fleeting weeks of open water, he planned to have Walter load the supplies aboard and run up the Kantishna and Bear Paw rivers, transporting them to a spot within fifty miles of the mountain. Movement by boat was infinitely easier than carrying the ton of material on dog sleds.

Harry Karstens checked in with a brief note, "I'm back in Fairbanks, and I'm ready whenever you are, Reverend."

"For your last trip with the *Pelican*," Hudson said to Walter, "you'll be taking those six children down to the school at Nenana next week. Check on those two cases that should have arrived from New York. Then load the cases and all the supplies we've accumulated at the school on board the *Pelican*, and take them here." He pointed to a spot on the map hanging on the wall of his room. "Have Johnny Fredson and Esaias make the trip with you. I'll give you a note to the principal."

Walter nodded cheerfully. The next week he was gone. In his care were six solemn-faced youngsters who tried to hide their fright as they went away for the first time to the native school at Nenana. Hudson watched them go, marveling at Walter's apparent unconcern with so great a task. Care of the children alone would have been a monumental undertaking. In addition he was piloting the leaky, balky *Pelican* down the mosquito-infested Yukon, to the juncture of the Tanana River and, winding along the latter stream, to Nenana. The journey would cover nearly 400 miles.

He was two weeks overdue in returning to Fort Yukon, and for the first time Hudson was alarmed for the safety of the young giant. Finally he leaped ashore from a strange launch and walked dejectedly up to the hospital.

"The *Pelican*, she broke down good this time. Whole engine blew up. I couldn't fix."

"What about the children?" Hudson demanded. "Where are they?"

"Oh, them kids, they're in school. This happen when me

and Johnny and Esaias start to take supplies on *Pelican* to place up on Kantishna."

Hudson sat down in relief, but immediately jumped to his feet. "We've got to get those supplies moved up the Kantishna before the freeze. It's either that—or postpone the climb another year. We'll get word down to Harry Karstens and ask him if he can help." He stopped pacing. "What about the two cases of goods from the outside? Did they arrive?"

Walter shook his head. "No. But there was river boat due next week. Last one for the season."

Karstens moved the supplies safely up the river to the cache, and escaped just before the freeze. He sent word that only one of the two expected cases had arrived from the States, and that one was too late to be carried with the other supplies up the river.

Hudson was rocked again with disappointment. "On our first sled trip down to Nenana we'll check the case. We've got to find out what's missing and then start ordering substitutes in Fairbanks." He bit his lip in vexation. The expedition was starting badly, and, as leader, he blamed himself.

But nothing would stop the preparation.

To Richard he wrote, "Much as I would like to have you join us next spring, I think it better that you remain in school. In your place I will ask Roger Tatum. Two of the young boys from the Nenana school, Johnny and Esaias, will handle our dog teams.

"If our attempt is successful," he continued, "I will return to the States early in the summer of 1913. I look forward to going with you to Sewanee and enrolling you in the college."

A month later the reply came, written in a laborious scrawl. "I am sorry. I would like to climb with you. I hope success for you and Walter. Your friend, Richard Bristol."

He continued his mission work, but there were a hundred

details that he must take on in addition. The first bitter winds of winter ripped over the land: the lakes froze to a smoky white, and the rivers hesitated, stilled, then were solid with ice. But it was not until early in February, 1913, that Hudson hastened with Walter down the trail to Nenana, shouting with a new vigor at the straining dogs. He forced himself first to visit with the teachers at the school; to talk with the forty children to whom he felt like a father, and to make plans for the building of a new addition. But always in the back of his mind was the shed in the rear where Walter had told him the packing case from New York was stored.

When the children had been called back to their classes he went with Walter and ripped off the wooden cover. He fingered the contents eagerly. "The tents are missing," he said, "and the climbing irons. But the boots are here, and the ice axes." He seized one of the sharp-pointed instruments and slashed it with boyish enthusiasm into the hardened ground. The point splintered and the handle shattered.

Walter picked up the shattered ax and looked at it in disgust. "Cheap."

Hudson nodded slowly. Had the ax shattered on the mountainside it could have meant death for the man who trusted his life to it. He looked with suspicion on the rest of the material. "They can't ruin the special food we ordered," he said dejectedly. "Let's make a list of everything here."

In Fairbanks, seventy-five miles from Nenana, he ordered new axes to be made, and new silk tents to replace those that had not arrived from New York. He was dismayed when he saw the dwindling figures in his bankbook. He had told Bishop Rowe that the expedition would cost one thousand dollars. He had not told him that the sum represented almost every dollar he had.

He had hoped to plunge into the final preparations of the trip, but suddenly word came that tragedy was brewing at the mission post at Tanana Crossing. Two women missionaries were isolated there, a schoolteacher and a nurse. Their winter's supply of food had been late in coming upriver, and the steamer, threatened by an early freeze-up, had dumped the supplies on the riverbank, a full hundred miles short of their destination at Tanana Crossing.

Roger Tatum, freed from his mission, had appeared in Fairbanks, anxious to be under way with the mountain venture. Hudson shook his head. "We've got to get that food to those women."

"If we wait too long," Walter Harper protested, "we won't get our own supplies to the base camp. We'll have a whole lot of mountain and no food. We won't ever climb that mountain."

Hudson shook his head. "You, Roger," he said, "take a team and start freighting those supplies into Tanana Crossing. Walter and I will be over next week and help you finish." But that night he was unable to sleep. He roused Walter. "We're leaving for Tanana Crossing at daybreak. See that the teams are ready."

They left Fairbanks at dawn, the dogs barking in protest, Walter stumbling along sullenly until Hudson spoke sharply to him. Then, as the miles sped by and the sleep dropped from Walter's eyes, he regained his good humor and soon was shouting in a high singsong voice, urging the dogs ahead. "That mountain," he called back over his shoulder to Hudson, "she's not going any place either. She still be there when we get ready to climb this year . . . next year . . . some year."

It was 250 miles along the winding ice-sheeted river to Tanana Crossing. They picked up the remainder of the food cache and followed the trail of Roger Tatum who had gone through the day before. The miles passed slowly. Each dragging day Hudson was sure the mountain climb would be postponed again. They swept into the mission post, and when the two faithful women showed them the unsalted rabbit that had been their only food, even Walter was impressed. "I am sorry, ma'am," he said, "we did not come sooner."

They rested for a day, then turned wearily about and plodded back over the 250 miles to Fairbanks. Harry Karstens had been busy in their absence, but the delays still piled up, and it was the seventeenth of March before the Hudson Stuck Expedition finally left the cheering youngsters who screamed farewells from the Indian school at Nenana. There were two sleds piled with supplies that were so wrapped up in protective cloth they seemed like corpses stretched on the sleds. There were fourteen yapping, excited dogs. There were four men. Two of them, Walter and Roger, were vigorous youths of twenty-one; Karstens was at the peak of physical condition at thirty-three; the two boys, Johnny and Esaias, were fourteen and tireless. Hudson, fifty years old, felt as though he were an anchor on the bursting enthusiasm of his companions. He vowed to himself that he would keep pace, that he would find the strength to keep marching side by side with the others.

There were two bright, wonderfully clear days on the trail across country to Toklat, with glimpses of McKinley to cheer them on. On Easter Sunday, 1913, Hudson held services for his own party and four men who were prospecting in the area. The next day they came to the Bearpaw River and the food cache Harry Karstens had brought down the previous September. Karstens jerked the covers off the cache and uttered a cry of dismay. "Those danged mice," he said, "they got into the cereals."

Walter leaned down and fingered a chewed box. "And they

liked rolled oats, too. All gone."

Hudson shrugged. "It's little loss. Thank goodness everything else is safe." He waved at the ton and a half of supplies. "Let's start moving it up."

The base of the mountain was fifty miles away, and rough, wild country hindered them. They started the endless physical exertion that was to be their companion from that day on. They went forward with the laden sleds, dumped supplies, retreated to the original cache, then started the long, wearying process all over again. All day and far into each night, the exhausting process continued while they relayed the supplies closer and closer to the base of the mountain.

Hudson felt himself staggering with fatigue. He watched himself closely. If he were to weaken he would be ruthless with himself and remain at the base camp, sending the others forward to the climb. But his heart burned with desire. He prayed for strength to continue.

They had as their goal a base camp at the 4000-foot altitude, and on April 10th they reached it. But that was only the beginning of the battle. Belmore Browne, in his third attempt on the mountain just a year before, had been forced back by starvation. Hudson was determined that they would be carrying ample food as they started to inch up the white wall that loomed above them.

By great good fortune they encountered an abundance of game just outside the base camp. Karstens killed a caribou, Walter a mountain sheep, and clear-eyed Esaias three caribou. They made pemmican, boiling the meat in huge chunks until it fell apart. Then they salted it, rolled it in melted butter and devised baseball-size chunks which they tossed aside to freeze. They made 200 of the meat baseballs, and Hudson was satisfied they would not die of hunger on the mountain.

Little Johnny Fredson was to stay at the base camp with

one of the dog teams, waiting and watching through what might be a month's vigil while the four men battled the mountain. Esaias was to return to Nenana with the other team, a journey fraught with danger because the ice on the streams was fast melting and the footing on the trails would be treacherous.

On the day of his departure, the fourteen-year-old boy abruptly knelt in the snow, and the others knelt with him, while Hudson prayed aloud for the safety of all of them. Then Esaias, flashing a wide grin, screamed at the dogs and started at a headlong pace down the mountain.

The five who were left watched the flying figures of the boy and the dogs dwindle and finally disappear.

12

They were alone only a short time. Up the mountainside, with a barking dog team, came an Indian and his wife, who carried on the sled a tiny infant. While Karstens looked on in wonder, the Indian tenderly lifted the child from the sled and approached Hudson. "I ask you baptize my baby."

Karstens came over. "Where'd you people come from?"

"Lake Minchumina."

"That's a hundred miles!"

The Indian nodded gravely. Karstens looked at Hudson, shaking his head in amazement. "If this fellow had waited two more weeks, he might have followed us right to the top of Mount McKinley!"

Hudson nodded. Inwardly, he, too, was amazed at the faith of the Indian. Quickly he melted snow in a clean pan and poured the warm water on the infant's head in the baptismal rite. "Go quickly," he said afterward, "and God keep you safe on the journey to your home."

"God keep you safe on the mountain," the Indian woman said. They were the first words she had spoken. The sled turned about and the odd party was soon gone from sight.

"Now then, Reverend," Karstens said briskly, "if you're sure there are no more baptisms or marriages or services you want to conduct, I say we ought to think about getting up this mountain." He looked suspiciously at the wall of ice and snow hanging over them. "Got a hunch, when we get to the top there'll be a Sunday school picnic that'll have beaten us up there."

Everything else was put aside as they turned toward the mountain.

Hudson explained the task to Johnny Fredson. "Other men have blazed the trail. We're going to use McPhee's Pass." He pointed to a break in the mountain wall. "The Fairbanks prospectors found it when they went to the North Peak three years ago. It will save us twenty miles of scrambling over the ice. Then we go straight up the glacier to the South Peak."

"Is easy," the boy said. "Over pass, up glacier." Then his forehead wrinkled. "How you know?"

"I've talked to those three men who nearly made it in 1910. And I've read the accounts of all those who tried it before them. I've studied charts and maps."

The boy flashed a wide grin. "Soon everybody climb Mount McKinley. You better hurry."

The base camp on Cache Creek was at the 4,000-foot elevation. McPhee's Pass, the short cut in the mountain wall that led to Muldrow Glacier, was three miles in length and climbed abruptly for 2,500 feet. Hudson and Karstens went ahead through the pass until they stood on the crumbling, dirty edge of the vast river of ice. At that point they were 6,500 feet above sea level. Hudson scribbled in the notebook he carried, "The glacier stretches before us, broad and level, a perfect road to the heart of the mountain. It is the highway of desire." Then he stuffed the notebook into his parka.

Harry Karstens shook his head. "Don't let this level stuff

fool you. From what the boys told me, up ahead it gets so rough you hate the sight of ice."

Hudson nodded. He turned and led the way back to the base camp. Once he looked over his shoulder. He knew how deceptive the river of ice was. He was willing to risk his own life in the conquest of the mountain, but perhaps he had been wrong to ask others to share that risk with him.

All five plunged into the task of moving to the first glacier camp, urging the dogs onward, making trip after trip with the food, instruments, equipment, firewood and the hundreds of wooden stakes that had been cut in order to mark the trail higher up on the mountain.

That task was completed; then once again it was repeated as they advanced everything to the next planned camp four miles deeper into the glacier. Their progress was slowing perceptibly, for the glacier ice, though still smooth, was becoming steeper. They started the relays early in the morning when the air was biting cold; they continued under a brilliant sun that made their work, despite the world of ice and snow about them, one of suffocating heat and irritating, endless glare; they worked into the night when the cold set in again, silently, fiercely, relentlessly.

The first few nights on the ice they were miserable, for the heat of bodies within the tent melted the ice and they woke each morning in aching, sodden misery. "You'd think a man'd learn, being in this country sixteen years like I have," Karstens said one morning when he woke, rubbing his aching joints, "but I never slept on an iceberg before." Then they placed a subfloor of boxes on the ice and, over that, a mat of thick caribou and bearhides, and once again they found comfort in exhausted sleep.

It took an entire week to move from the base camp, through the steep McPhee Pass and up the first four miles of ice. Suddenly the smoothness and comparative ease were gone. The ice collapsed into a nightmare of rough, jagged blocks, treacherous crevasses and yawning chasms.

"We keep plunging ahead like this," Karstens said, "and one of us is going to disappear into an ice bucket. It'll be a one-way trip. I looked down and it must've been 200 feet to the bottom."

"We'll split up," Hudson said. "Three will go ahead, roped together, and the man in the lead will probe the ice with a pole to see if it's safe. The other two, in the lead party, will carry stakes and mark the trail. That will leave two men to keep freighting supplies with the dog team."

The next morning Karstens, Johnny Fredson and Roger Tatum moved ahead into the tossing sea of ice. Hudson and Walter bent to the backbreaking task of freighting the supplies higher on the glacier. Each was roped to a sled, in order to give help to the straining, slipping dogs. Hudson was pulling like a pack horse, head down, eyes half shut, slipping and sliding as he fought for footing.

"Archdeacon! Archdeacon!" He heard Walter's cry of alarm, and he felt a touch of fear. If anything should happen to Walter! He threw off the rope, staggered, then groped his way forward over the ice.

Walter was pointing to a crevasse beside the sled. "Snowball!" he yelled. "He slipped out of the harness and fell down the hole." Dropping to his hands and knees into the snow, he peered cautiously downward. "He's still alive. I can see him. About twenty-five feet down."

Hudson threw himself flat on the ice beside Walter. He could see Snowball stretched on a ledge, whimpering piteously. Hudson's heart ached. He was affectionate with his dog teams. Four years before, when the unreliable but thoroughly lovable Jimmy, the Fake, had disappeared in the middle of a blizzard, Snowball had moved up to take his place as lead dog. In all he had been with Hudson for over 10,000 miles of Alaskan trails.

Walter raced back to the sled and began to untie the safety rope. He tossed the end to Hudson. "You hold tight. I can slip down the crevasse and get him out."

"No."

Walter looked at Hudson in astonishment. "You going to leave him there. To die?"

"I can't risk letting you go down there. Come away." He strode back to the sled and, taking up the strain on the rope, called the remaining dogs to their feet. As they struggled past the crevasse he could hear faint whimperings from Snowball.

Later that afternoon, when they had freighted the load of wood and supplies up to the new cache on the glacier, they waited impatiently for Karstens, Johnny and Roger to return from marking the forward trail. They explained what had happened to Snowball; then, leaving Johnny behind to prepare the evening meal, the others hurried to the crevasse. Snowball greeted them with weak whimpers. Walter tied one end of the rope securely about his waist. Karstens and Roger held tight to the other end and dug their heels deep into the ice to take up the strain. Then Walter went down, hand over hand.

He sent the dog up first. Hudson, peering over the edge, could see the Indian youth pressed tight against the wall of the crevasse far below him, trying not to betray his fear. Then the rope came down again. Walter tied it about his waist, and scrambled quickly to safety.

For a moment, Hudson stood immobilized, his eyes shut, breathing a prayer of thanksgiving. Then he pulled himself away, rubbing his stiffened muscles as he went. "We better hurry back; the cook will be getting impatient."

Every waking moment was filled with activity, yet progress was slow. Six weeks after leaving the mission school at Nenana they were still struggling up the face of Muldrow Glacier, the most awesome part of their journey still before them.

It was unending toil, the most laborious period Hudson had ever spent in his life. The weather was excellent, even too good, for the incessant sunshine became almost a menace. A new type of amber eyeglasses saved them from the most dangerous effects of sun glinting on the endless expanse of snow and ice, but the rays burned their skin. Karstens, in particular, was made miserable by a combination of sunburn and skin rash that kept him in constant torment, yet he never complained.

To Hudson, who watched Karstens in open admiration, the prospector was a calm, matter-of-fact giant, a tireless man filled with a sure confidence that they would conquer McKinley. It was that confidence that gave strength to all of them and overcame some of Hudson's misgivings.

Even Walter, in excellent physical condition, watched in awe as Karstens whipped heavy loads about on the glacier and pulled the overcrowded sled effortlessly up the steep grades in his search for safe routes over the treacherous ice bridges.

Roger Tatum, in displays of youthful exuberance, contested constantly with Walter, his twin in age, in feats of endurance, where one mistake or the show of weakness could mean death.

Even Johnny was caught up in the excitement, at times exhorting the dogs with his shrill, boyish voice, then dropping back to plead with Hudson, "I want to go right to the top of mountain." He held out his right arm, shapeless in the parka that enclosed it. "I'm strong."

"Say 'please,' " Walter interrupted. "Don't they teach you manners at that school?"

"Please, sir," Johnny repeated. "I want to go right to the top. Please, sir."

Hudson shook his head. "We couldn't make the climb if someone were not waiting at the base camp with a fire and warm food. Our lives will be depending on you, Johnny."

The boy's face showed his disappointment. He pulled his parka hood tight, then, stumbling, ran ahead to keep pace with the team. Watching him, Hudson thought of Richard, who had had that same intensity, when he had first met him, years ago. For a few moments his thoughts drifted 4,000 miles away to Richard at his schoolbooks, his dark eyes intent on the straight lines of print. But he slipped, and was brought back abruptly to the task at hand.

It was on the ninth of May, when they had penetrated as far into the glacier as it was possible to take the dog teams, that Hudson called Johnny to his side. "You'll go back now and wait for us. We should be able to get to the top and back to you at the base camp in two weeks' time."

The boy nodded. He readied the empty sled, then obediently began the descent. Hudson beckoned to Roger Tatum. "We'll go with him part way down the mountain."

They journeyed with the boy, but there was little said, for Johnny was fighting tears of disappointment. When they reached the point where Hudson knew that smooth ice gave him a fair highway back to the camp, they parted. The boy mumbled a few words, but kept his face hidden in his parka. Hudson and Roger watched him grow smaller in the distance, then they turned and started back to Walter and Karstens.

Now they were forced to carry on their backs in endless relays all the food, firewood, instruments, bedding and tents that they would need as they toiled higher and higher. They carried their very lives in the packs strapped to their backs. Save for one bewildered rabbit at the 10,000-foot elevation, all game had long since disappeared. If they were to live, they must carry their food with them. If they were to be warm, they must have the firewood; if they were to survive the inevitable blizzards which would come out of the presently blue sky, they must have the tents, and the sleeping bags, and the robes, and the changes of clothing.

One day, as exhausting as all those that went before, they carried their loads higher on the mountain, treading in the steps carved for them by the indomitable Karstens. At noon they reached a spot selected for a temporary cache. They threw off their packs, unloaded them, then covered equipment and food with the large tent. They ate briefly and then rested. Karstens and Hudson smoked their pipes, sitting in the snow, their backs against the mound of goods they had just carried up. Across from them Walter and Roger stretched full length in the snow, their arms spread wide as though trying to embrace the fleeting rest period.

Reluctantly Hudson signaled Karstens. They knocked the ashes from their pipes and called to the two young men. Then all trudged downhill to the previous night's camp and the supplies that must still be carried forward.

Late that afternoon they were once more toiling upward. Hudson was so numb with fatigue that he kept his head down and his eyes half closed, focusing on the pinpricks made by the ice crampons worn by Walter who was immediately ahead. Suddenly there was a cry from Roger. "We've got company. Look ahead there to the cache!"

They raised their eyes and followed his pointing finger. A thin wisp of smoke eddied above the ice.

"It's impossible!" Karstens said.

"Perhaps," Hudson said, trying to hide his disappointment, "another party is on the mountain." Then he straightened. "Let's hurry and greet them. They may be hungry. We can feed them."

Walter tossed aside his pack and started to run up the slope. "Is no visitors," he yelled back over his shoulder. "The tent is on fire!"

Fire! Fire high on the slopes of Mount McKinley! Hudson tossed off his pack and ran to catch up with the three who sped before.

It was true. Sparks from either Hudson's or Karstens' pipe had ignited the silk tent used as temporary cover over the supplies. Walter and Roger threw themselves almost bodily on the flames and beat them out. Then they hurled scoops of snow and loose ice on the smoldering embers. Karstens and Hudson scattered the remnants on the ice, kicking and stomping on the glowing coals.

For a few moments no one spoke. Disaster was spread about them. The expedition had probably ended with one careless flick of a tobacco spark. "We'll take an inventory to see what we've lost," Hudson said quietly. "We must hurry before it gets dark."

It was a roll call of disaster. The tent was ruined. All the sugar was gone, all the powdered milk, the baking powder, the prunes, raisins, dried apples, a case of pilot bread, a sackful of woolen socks and gloves, and all the photographic film for Hudson's camera.

Karstens kicked dolefully at a blackened sack. "Leastways we can't make the same mistake twice. All the tobacco is burnt up."

Dark shadows were gathering quickly in the mountain hanging over them. The bitter cold night was racing forward to enclose the battered disconsolate group. They looked to Hudson.

He lifted his eyes to the peak that was already fading behind the clouds. "We'll eat," he said, "and then sleep. And we'll pray. In the morning we'll make a decision—to go forward, or to admit defeat and go down off the mountain while we're still able to do so."

13

When they had finished the monotonous evening meal they crawled into their sleeping bags and slept soundly, almost ignoring the loss that had overwhelmed them. In the few fleeting seconds before sleep came, Hudson thought dimly of the added disaster if a blizzard should come in the night and find them without shelter.

At three in the morning he stirred. Suddenly he was wide awake. He alone must make the decision. He crawled out and stood upright in the light snow that had fallen. The faint pencil marks of the new day were spreading on the eastern horizon.

The stars were of an unusual brilliance, one in particular was so large it seemed almost distorted. He moved away from the snow-covered sleeping bags that marked his three companions, and knelt and prayed. Above him the sky lightened; a red line broadened on the horizon. The sun broke through, shone brightly, then immediately went behind a pall of clouds. When Hudson rose and went back to the temporary camp the three were sitting upright, as though reluctant to leave the warmth of the sleeping bags. They looked at him expectantly.

"You and Roger," he said to Walter, "will go back to the base camp and get whatever you can to replace what we've lost in the fire. Karstens and I will explore the ridge up to the next glacier."

They parted company almost casually, the two young men disappearing down the glacier over which they had traveled so many times; Hudson and Karstens lifting their eyes to the ridge that awaited them.

They were camped at the head of Muldrow Glacier. They were faced now by an ice wall 4000 feet high, a towering, frozen Niagara. It would be necessary to climb the wall before they were on the upper glacier that presumably would lead directly into the peak.

"There was a ridge," Karstens said, puzzled, "that connected the two glaciers. McGonogill told me they scrambled up in one day. Carrying that crazy fourteen-foot signal pole, too."

"Browne and Parker mentioned the ridge also," Hudson replied. "It took two days for them to go up it. But when they climbed last year they were carrying supplies and instruments."

They turned a corner and saw the worst ice they had yet encountered. As far as the eye could see, stretching upward in a confused mass, was a nightmare of ice boulders. Karstens whistled. "It's impossible. I don't believe anyone ever climbed that mass."

Hudson scanned the surface, his heart sinking. "When Browne retreated," he said, "he told of an earthquake that shook the mountain." He pointed to the shattered ice—some of it weird cubes weighing hundreds of tons—that perched precariously on every side. "The ridge has been chewed up. There's nothing left of the passage."

For hours they squirmed through the mass of ice cakes,

many times progressing clumsily up a deceptive passage only to emerge in a maze worse than the original. They were like two ants seeking a passageway through a forest that had been beaten into confusion by a hurricane. Then a mist came rolling over the mountain, gray cotton balls seeking every hollow, blinding their attempts at trail blazing. They were forced back to the foot of the ice heap. They retreated to the temporary camp, just in time to help Walter and Roger, bent almost double under heavy packs.

The next day the four sat like tailors about a small fire, fashioning a crude tent from torn canvas sled covers. The tent they made was a wretched shelter six feet by seven, and only three feet, six inches high.

"Any man wants to turn over," Walter said solemnly, "must count one, two, three. Then we all turn."

Roger held a pair of socks he had made from the camel's-hair lining of a sleeping bag. "No complaints from the man who has to wear these. You won't find stitching like this if you look the whole world over."

They were busy all day making sorry substitutes for the material lost in the fire. When they prepared for sleep they were content. In the morning they could renew the assault.

But they were no longer masters of the journey. The weather, which had been so helpful, suddenly changed. The wind howled, and snow beat down upon them, and the peaks overhead were completely obscured in the wind-whipped clouds.

Every morning they woke and crawled from the low tent and looked about, hopeful they could go forward. And every morning the mist closed in, followed by high winds and heavy snow.

Walter looked at the gray clouds that curled on the mountainside far below them. "Down there," he said, pointing to the hidden valleys and the vast stretch of interior Alaska, "the ice is breaking. The trees are getting some leaves. Up here," he continued, "is winter forever."

They were not idle during the long, cold days of waiting. Every piece of equipment was checked and checked again. In brief moments of relaxation Hudson read for the fifth time the thin India paper copy of *Lorna Doone*. Walter, without too great a display of enthusiasm, wrote patiently as Hudson dictated to him. Then for several hours, sitting hunched under the damp tent cover as the wind howled outside, he raised his voice in a quaint singsong as he practiced reading aloud from the Scriptures. Not content with that, Hudson put him through short exercises in geography and history and physics.

"When we come off the mountain," Hudson said to Walter, "I'm taking you back to Massachusetts with me. You're ready for preparatory school." He lapsed into silence, thinking of the reunion that would take place with Richard Bristol.

Roger Tatum, sprawled on his back, rested a copy of the Scriptures on his broad chest and hour after hour wordlessly memorized the verses. Harry Karstens, trapped in the midst of the intellectual activity 11,000 feet up on the side of Mount McKinley, placed a sheet of notepaper on a tin can of tea. On the paper he drew and redrew the design of an advanced motorboat engine that he hoped someday to build.

Outside the wind howled. Though they tried to ignore it, they were prisoners on the mountain. Only the pitiful heap of food supplies, the coal oil for the Primus lamp, and the dwindling scraps of firewood that they had hauled so laboriously for twenty miles, remained as a hope for victory.

"Listen!" Roger Tatum sat upright, his head bumping the roof of the tent.

The wind had stilled. There was a thin trickle, then a rattle, followed by a terrifying roar. The four men tumbled out of the tent just in time to see an avalanche taking strength on the peak high above them. The roar increased, and the clouds of snow and ice dust billowed on the mountainside. For a few uncertain moments the onrushing torrent aimed straight at them, then bounced and fell into a diverting gully, and rushed with an angry roar into a hidden section of Muldrow Glacier.

Finally they decided that the weather would never again be as good as it had been at the start of the journey. They went out into the wind, and, with Karstens leading, started to scramble up the ice blocks. It was necessary for them to cut steps into the chunks, advancing a little, then retreating. Again, as always, each man was relaying forty-pound packs of supplies as he went higher.

For three endless weeks they hacked their way up the shattered ridge leading to the higher glacier. At times it was so cloudy they could not see ahead to plan the course, and were forced to remain in camp. Once a high wind chased them from the ridge; another time it was a dense snowstorm. Always, in threatening chorus, were the rattles and roars of the avalanches.

They would climb 100 feet, 200, 500, in a long, laborious day that started sometimes at five in the morning and did not end until fourteen hours later.

On the 25th of May they were at the 13,000-foot elevation —but they had climbed only 1,500 feet above the spot where the fire had threatened them.

Small things took on great proportions. Their sugar began to run out. They were reduced to tasteless hot cakes. The savory warmth of cocoa that had sustained them suddenly was gone. What little sugar was left was saved miserly for tea and coffee. Then the sugar was entirely gone, and they looked with distaste on cups of liquid that had suddenly become almost revolting. Even Hudson, who had spent a lifetime concealing his feelings, admitted, "Never in my life have I longed for something as much as a teaspoonful of sugar."

The only compensation, as they watched the days dribble by in endless toil, was the view of Alaska that spread beneath them when the winds stilled and the clouds rolled away. Those moments were rare. Wind and snow and clouds ruled the mountain.

On May 30th they dragged themselves wearily up the last few feet of the ridge and made camp in Parker Pass at 15,000 feet. It took two days to move through the sloping pass. On June 2nd they were standing on the Grand Basin, the smooth floor of the upper glacier that led to the peak of Mount McKinley. The next day, in a sudden burst of energy, they made camp in the middle of the glacier at the 16,500-foot mark. The peak was less than 4,000 feet above them.

Walter looked upward speculatively. "You look at your watch, Archdeacon," he said without turning his head, "and I run up. You time me."

Roger Tatum came by him and crouched like a runner waiting for the starting gun. "You'll have to beat me."

Their joy was short-lived. As they moved out into the wide, shallow valley, the wind raced across it with a killing force. The shallowness of the basin in itself was a deception. At places it became so steep that it was necessary to continue cutting steps in the ice.

They were still relaying food and equipment. Generally Karstens and Roger were in the lead, roped together, making sure of the trail. Hudson and Walter came behind, toting forty-pound packs of supplies up for a few hundred feet, then returning to get what was left at the previous night's camp. There still remained between 250 and 300 pounds of supplies. It meant at least three round trips for each creeping advance upward.

Walter grunted as he shouldered his pack. "Lucky we keep eating. Each day, little less we got to carry."

Hudson made no reply. He became dizzy, staggered and almost fell. He looked quickly ahead to see if Walter had noticed, but the young man was bent to his load, digging into the ice. Hudson rested a few moments, trying to clear the dizziness that beset him. He placed one foot forward, then fell on his face. He and Walter were roped together for safety, and the fall jerked Walter backward. He scrambled about, saw Hudson and plodded awkwardly to his side, tugging at his parka. "What happened? You slip? Are you hurt?"

"No. I'm not hurt." Hudson gratefully accepted Walter's proffered help. He struggled to his feet. "Let's get ahead."

They moved upward, Walter continually turning his head to check on Hudson. The latter just as studiously avoided Walter's gaze. He knew that he was fighting to breathe, that the ice fields about them swam in slow circular motions, that he was in danger at any moment of pitching on his face. He took a dozen steps forward, stopped, went forward again.

When they reached the two trailmakers he was unable to speak. He saw Walter go ahead and talk to Roger and Karstens. Then Karstens came back, his face puckered with anxiety.

"You going to make it all right, Reverend?"

Hudson sat heavily in the snow. He nodded. "I'm going to make it. All I need is a bit of rest." He looked upward at the summit of McKinley. So close! What if he were forced to stay behind while the others went ahead!

"It's the altitude," Karstens said gruffly. "Tell you what. Suppose you just hang onto the barometer. Me and the two boys can lug the rest of this stuff. Just a hop, skip and a jump up to the top. We'll make it."

Hudson drew in his breath. He nodded in agreement. He watched in envy as the three divided his pack among them, swung the weight easily on their younger, stronger shoulders and started up again.

On Thursday, June 5th, they made camp at the 17,500-foot elevation. The following day they moved ahead 500 feet. Hudson was stumbling, gasping for breath, his head bowed in utter exhaustion.

The next day they would make the final dash up the last 2700 feet to the summit.

That night they huddled in the tent, their hands outstretched to the thin yellow flame of the little roaring Primus. It burned coal oil that had been packed laboriously up the side of the mountain. Hudson looked at the stove reflectively. "Maybe we carried up too much in the way of supplies," he said. "We've got enough for another two weeks. Three weeks, if we had to go on a starvation diet." He shook his head doubtfully. "I wanted to be sure. Browne was even closer than this when he was forced back last year. He and his men were starving."

Karstens started to crawl into his sleeping bag. "If the weather turns bad and we get pinned into this tent, we might wish we had even more food left over."

The other two crept into their sleeping bags, but Hudson remained crouched over the stove, trying to suck its warmth into his body. He was ill, but he did not want to alarm the others. Pulling a blanket about his shoulders, he prayed quietly until he nodded to sleep.

At five in the morning, broad daylight, they were out of the tent, stamping their feet and shaking their arms against the bitter minus twenty-one-degree cold. Walter, still munching on a great chunk of pemmicam meat ball, faced toward the peak and started to climb.

Hudson was in the rear. He was violently ill, choking, gasping, staggering as he reached automatically ahead to get a firm stance in the ice and pull himself forward. Roger Tatum, looking back, silently reached for the barometer Hudson carried in a case slung over his shoulder. Hudson looked up gratefully, nodding his thanks.

They climbed for six hours, tortured by wind that pulled at them relentlessly, trying to defeat them in the final move on the mountain. Hudson blinked his eyes as a wave of pain flowed over him. He recognized the spot, within a few hundred feet of the peak, where Browne had been turned back, defeated, the year before. Walter was still plunging forward. Hudson crept after.

At one-thirty in the afternoon of June 7th, Walter scrambled over the lip of a shallow cup of snow that marked the peak. Immediately behind him came Karstens and Tatum. Hudson was below, at the end of the safety rope that bound the four of them. He was about to sink to the snow—defeated. Walter and Tatum seized the rope and hauled upward. They pulled Hudson over the lip of the basin, and he fell unconscious at their feet.

It was seventy-seven days since they had started from the foot of the mountain.

Hudson revived quickly and struggled to his feet. He breathed deeply, gasping. Impulsively he thrust out a gloved hand, first to Karstens, then to Walter, then to Roger. "Thank God we made it safely," he said. He lifted his eyes to the clear sky above them. "Thank you, Almighty God," he said, "for granting us our heart's desire, for bringing us safely to the top of Your great mountain."

Then he turned briskly about. "The instruments," he said to Walter. To Roger he said, "We won't need to set up the instrument tent. But have it ready in case it should start to snow."

For an hour they worked quickly, almost silently, taking scientific readings on the instruments. They checked and rechecked, and as Hudson called out the readings, Roger entered them with numbed fingers into a notebook.

Finally it was finished. They waited for another half hour, looking at the world spread beneath them—the wonderland of Alaska, white snow streaked with the green of tundra and the blue-black ribbons of rivers winding in valleys in another world below them. Straight out were the endless sharp-spined peaks of sister mountains that stood in homage about Mount McKinley.

"Raise the flag, Roger," Walter said.

From his pocket Roger drew a small flag he had fashioned from two handkerchiefs. He fastened them to the pole of the dismantled instrument tent. The Stars and Stripes stood out rigid in the wind.

Below the flag Walter fastened a smaller horizontal section of the tent pole. It formed a cross above the mountain.

"We'll sing the *Te Deum,*" Hudson said quietly. Then, lifting his head, his eyes closed, he sang, "We praise Thee, O God!"

The three battered adventurers grouped about him, the wind almost tearing the notes from their lips as they were formed, and answered him in song, "Heaven and earth are full of Thy glory!"

At three o'clock they turned and started down the mountain. By five o'clock they were back at the camp they had left twelve hours before. As he crawled into his sleeping bag

Hudson said to Karstens, "In all my life I've never known a day so full of toil and distress and exhaustion." He pulled the sleeping bag cover almost over his head before continuing, "But I've never known a day so full of happiness and gratification."

Karstens didn't answer. He was fast asleep.

14

It took only two days to scramble down the mountain to the base camp where Johnny Fredson waited. There was a joyous reunion, then the four mountaineers, almost savage in their assault, turned on the freshly killed caribou, the coffee, and, most of all, the sugar the young boy had saved.

The next morning they started on the sixty-mile hike back to Eureka, the nearest settlement. There they borrowed a battered flatboat and floated in luxury down the Bearpaw River, to the Kantishna, then to the Tanana, and finally the Yukon. At the telegraph office in Tanana, Hudson sent a message to a Seattle newspaper, and the world knew for the first time, thirteen days after the event, that Mount McKinley had finally been conquered.

Hudson, in his usual blunt manner, always said the epic climb posed no special mountaineering difficulties. The biggest problem, he said, was in getting under way, transporting the necessary supplies and equipment to the base camp. Yet not for another nineteen years, until 1932, did anyone else reach the summit of McKinley. To date slightly more than 100 men have reached the summit. Airplanes now land at the

7,500-foot elevation, bringing heavy equipment and tons of supplies to those who make the assault. On one occasion, during the rescue of a stranded party, an airplane landed in a smooth spot at the 14,200-foot mark, accomplishing in minutes what had taken Hudson and his party almost seventy-days of desperate struggle. On still another occasion, when an injured climber was dying on the side of the mountain, a helicopter, straining to its utmost, reached the 17,500-foot altitude and removed the injured man.

The only thing unchanged is the weather, brutal and menacing and unpredictable today as it was fifty years ago. Despite radios and airplanes and helicopters and the most elaborate modern mountaineering equipment, men are still dying in their attempts to creep up the flanks of the mountain.

The hundred who were successful engaged in heroic efforts, and all of them reaped the reward of conquest. But Hudson and his three companions were the first.

Back at the mission at Fort Yukon, he shrugged off the trip. He had been granted a lifelong desire; he had climbed the mountain and now it was over. He turned to his people.

Bishop Rowe, however, insisted that Hudson go outside to the States, to speak to audiences throughout the nation who were eager to hear of the McKinley adventure.

He went reluctantly, for the needs of the missions were many, but he was buoyed by the knowledge that the money he would earn lecturing would be of inestimable aid in taking care of those needs.

He brought with him Walter Harper, and enrolled him in the school in Massachusetts where Richard Bristol was studying. Hudson was obsessed with the need for developing leaders among the natives. He was convinced that higher education was the prime need. Richard was already preparing; Walter would follow him into the preparatory school, and then into the University of the South. In his precise accounting of the years to come, Hudson had already determined that Johnny Fredson, in his time, would follow the paths to be blazed by the others. These were the men, Hudson said to himself, who would take over the task of leading the Alaska natives to their rightful place in the territory.

The reunion with Richard was stilted, almost strained. As always, Hudson felt that a wall existed between him and the young Indian. Walter, the direct opposite in temperament, was loud in his appreciation for the exciting turn of events in his life. He brushed back the tears when Hudson said goodby. Richard Bristol shook hands gravely.

As he toured the United States, repeating the saga of the Mount McKinley adventures to the thousands who listened in rapt attention, Hudson could never entirely put from his mind the thought of the young man upon whom he looked as a son, and yet who looked upon him as almost a stranger.

He had been back in Alaska for more than a year when he received a short note from Richard Bristol. "I do not care to continue school. I am going to Montreal and join the Canadian Army."

It was the winter of 1914 and the thunder of the new war in Europe was already beginning to roll over the entire world. The thunder caught up with Richard Bristol and he was carried from Massachusetts to Canada, to England and to France. He died in the opening battle of the Somme on July 1, 1916.

It took nearly two months for the word to come back to Hudson. He was striding from the riverbank to the mission hospital at Fort Yukon when the letter was handed to him. He was rigid as he read the short message. Then, stuffing the letter into his pocket, he went into his room at the hospital and closed the door. He knelt by his sparse iron bed, his hands clenched, and gave vent to his grief.

When he came from his room he was clear-eyed, erect. The loss he had suffered he kept locked within himself.

Immediately he began to make plans for the most daring of his overland journeys. "I am archdeacon of the Yukon and the Arctic," he said persuasively to Bishop Rowe in outlining the plan, "yet I have never been able to visit our mission at Point Hope on the Chukchi, or to visit with the natives on the Arctic slope."

"I think you should visit them," the bishop agreed. "But why can't you do it as government officials do—travel on the revenue cutter when it makes its annual trip to that area? I'd have no difficulty in arranging with Washington. . . ."

Hudson shook his head. "In the summer, when the cutter goes along the coast, the people are scattered, hunting and fishing, getting ready for the winter. I want to go up and visit them when they are leading normal lives."

Bishop Rowe stroked his chin thoughtfully. "How old are you, Hudson?"

"Fifty-three. No." he corrected hastily, "fifty-two. I don't pay much attention to birthdays."

The bishop nodded. "I notice." He shook his head doubtfully. "You'd be gone six months, traveling a country few white men have ever covered." He sighed and picked up the map Hudson had spread before them. He traced the penciled route, a vast sweep over the northern part of Alaska that first retraced the original route Hudson had taken years before over to Kotzebue Sound on his first long Alaskan journey. But there the trips parted abruptly. This new venture would call for a swing north to the mission at Point Hope, then a tracing of the bulging Alaska coast line around to Point Barrow, the northernmost inhabited spot in Alaska, then a run along the ice-covered Arctic Ocean and the Alaska shore line to its meeting with Canadian territory. The final leg would be an abrupt turn south along the frozen shells of the Firth River, the Coleen and the Porcupine to the starting point at Fort Yukon.

The journey would take six months.

The bishop put the map aside. "It's too late for you to start off this year, isn't it?"

"Yes. I'd need a great deal of time to get ready. When the rivers freeze next year—that is when I would leave."

Bishop Rowe nodded abruptly. "All right. You have my blessing. Unless something drastic happens, you can go."

In April, 1917, the United States entered World War I, but the event seemed far removed from the cluster of villages along the Yukon. Hudson wrote to Walter, "I would like you to join me on the trip along the Arctic slope. I have misgivings about taking you away from school for six months, but I do not feel I could make the journey without your assistance."

Walter returned in the summer of 1917, and Hudson marveled at the subtle changes that were taking place in the twenty-four-year-old man. Already he walked among the admiring natives as one who would lead them.

Walter went up the Charley River with a younger boy on a twelve-day hunting trip, returning with more than a ton of meat, enough to supply the hospital at Fort Yukon for most of the winter.

Suddenly he fell ill with typhoid fever, and for a week he was close to death. Hudson was at his bedside constantly, watching as Dr. Burke tended the patient. He knew the trip to the Arctic was out of the question. He would stay with Walter.

Then the Indian youth recovered wtih astonishing rapidity.

Grafton Burke turned to Hudson. "He's not only going to live—if you can postpone your trip for ten days he might be able to go with you."

They left on November 7, 1917, on a bitterly cold morning when the fresh ice was strong on the Yukon. They left before dawn, not only to get the full benefit of the short daylight hours on the trail, but also to avoid the solemn, time-consuming farewells that the natives always pressed upon Hudson. It was as though they sensed the dangers into which he almost eagerly ventured.

Several times they became lost, and survival came only because of the fearlessness with which they met the danger. They were exposed to cold that should have killed them, yet they continued on, and when they found shelter and warmth, the life that remained in them was nursed back to full strength.

They knew exhaustion from endless days on the trail, but each time the exhaustion drained from Hudson when he stood before the uplifted faces in some crowded snow hut. Waiting for the chanting singsong of the interpreter he spoke very slowly. "I am Hudson Stuck, archdeacon of the Episcopal church. I am sent to speak to you of a merciful Father, One who regards all of us as His children."

As he spoke to them, he marveled at the trust they displayed, the rapt attention they gave to the halting words relayed through the interpreter. At night, when he stretched out on a shelf within the hut, trying to find sleep in the crowded night noises about him, he prayed, "Lord, I do believe. Increase my faith."

The warmth of his reception gave him strength to continue the journey along the desolate shore of Alaska that faces on the tumbled ice of the Arctic Ocean. Month followed month. It was not until April, 1918, six months from his departure, that he returned to Fort Yukon.

Walter stayed with Hudson throughout the spring and the summer. Then he came to him one day and told him of his love for a young Indian girl at Fort Yukon. Hudson joined them in marriage, and a few weeks later, Walter and his bride left for the States. He was to enter the University of the South at Sewanee and begin his long preparation for a career as a medical missionary. The two young people sailed south from Skagway on the ill-fated steamer, the *Princess Sophia*.

The dedication in one of Hudson's books reads:

In loving memory of Walter Harper, companion of this and many other journeys, strong, gentle, brave and clean, who was drowned in the Lynn Canal when the *Princess Sophia* foundered with her entire company, on October 25, 1918.

The winter of 1918-1919 Hudson remained most of the time at Fort Yukon. There was much to do, he told himself, yet there were moments when he confessed that the ordeal of taking to the trails without the strong help of Walter was too much for him. He was not a prisoner, and he made the necessary visitations to the missions within a short radius. But no longer did he gaze fascinated at the wide sweep of unexplored Alaska territory, planning for trips into the unknown.

In the spring of 1919 he received word that he was to be given the Sir George Back award, granted annually by the Royal Geographical Society for the improvement and diffusion of geographical knowledge. The award was being tendered to Hudson, the letter said, for his travels in Alaska and for the ascent of Mount McKinley. It would be presented at the society's headquarters in London, England.

It was a tremendous honor yet Hudson was reluctant to leave the Yukon for the journey to England. Then Bishop Rowe spoke to him of the desperate need for someone to go before the United States Congress in Washington, D.C., to plead for the rights of the natives in the tremendous power struggle going on over the salmon fishery rights.

"The congressmen will listen to you," the bishop urged. "You can tell them how these traps being set by the canning companies are keeping the salmon from coming upstream, how the catch is getting smaller each year. You can go on from there to England. I would appreciate this very much."

So Hudson agreed to go. He took Johnny Fredson with him and, like Richard and Walter before him, had him enrolled in the preparatory school in Massachusetts as a preliminary move to later enrollment in the University of the South at Sewanee. He, too, was marked to become a leader of his people.

Hudson then went south by train to Washington. He strode vigorously into the paneled hearing room of the committee that was considering the fisheries bill. When called upon, he spoke urgently of the needs of the natives, of their helplessness before the onslaught of the white men who descended upon the land like a swarm of locusts. "Twenty years ago," he said, "it was the horde of gold prospectors who ravaged the natives; today it is the large corporations, like the salmon trust, who are preying upon the rightful heritage of the natives."

He rose from the witness chair. "I have watched calamities overtaking the native people. For fifteen years I have lived with them and shared with them disasters that white men brought upon them. Gentlemen," he cried, "the fishing rights belong to Alaskans! The territory needs the revenue from the fisheries to build homes for our people, to build schools, to establish civilization! Don't give in to the fish trusts! They are robbing Alaska!"

The committee listened respectfully—then voted against the natives and in favor of the outside fish trusts.

It was a bitter disappointment for Hudson. He hurried to New York and boarded the ship that took him to England.

It had been thirty years since Hudson had left London. He walked now almost as a stranger in the city. The wet streets, the red-brick buildings, the dark iron bridges, the fog and the rain, and the yellow daffodils in Hyde Park were all the same, but he himself was different. He was fifty-five years old. There was no reason why he should not live for another twenty vigorous years in the Yukon, but he felt utterly weary. His experience before the congressional committee was for him a personal defeat.

He walked slowly along Aldersgate Street, then turned into St. Paul's Cathedral and knelt silently in a darkened corner. He rebuked himself because his prayers came so haltingly. He could think only of Richard and Walter.·

At the Royal Geographical Society meeting where he was given the Back award, he spoke only briefly, acknowledging his thanks for the honor tendered him. That night he boarded a ship and started the long trip back to the Yukon.

In the summer of 1920 he journeyed along the river. The progress of the Alaskan missions under Bishop Rowe had been solid, and Hudson was quietly content with the part he had played. Three missions had been increased to twenty-one; one school had become nine. But there was much more to be done.

Each new winter rolls over Alaska like a noiseless wave breaking over a beach. It starts with the glint of fresh ice on the Arctic shore, then flows southward. Chunks of ice start bobbing in the Meade River, the Colville and the Turner. Birds that can flee race ahead of it. There is a period of faint hesitation, then a skin of ice leaps almost visibly across the rivers.

The Yukon may be a solid river of ice in October; then again it may be freezing, but free, until sometime in November.

Winter came exceptionally early in 1920. Hudson returned to Fort Yukon, hurried in his final boat trip by the daily threat of the freeze-up. He walked slowly up to the hospital and to his room. He was coughing and his drawn face was flushed with fever. In a few hours Dr. Burke diagnosed his illness as pneumonia. The disease advanced quickly, as though it had seized on a moment of weakness. At dawn of October 10, 1920, Hudson Stuck died.

When the word reached Johnny Fredson, the Indian went out into the Massachusetts hills and cut down a large pine tree. He formed a cross and carried it into the school chapel. Johnny's long struggle finally carried him to successful graduation from the University of the South. He went back to the Yukon as Hudson had wished, but he died within a few years of his return.

Harry Karstens became a well-known figure in Alaska, the first superintendent of the McKinley National Park. Roger Tatum completed his studies, was ordained and spent his life in the Episcopal ministry before retiring to his home in Nashville, Tennessee.

The hospital at Fort Yukon was renamed the Hudson Stuck Memorial Hospital in memory of the man who had done most for the natives along the river. It closed in 1957 when a government hospital made it no longer necessary. Even the closing was a moment of triumph for Hudson. Bit by bit, all the reforms he had demanded, all the aid he had asked for the natives, came about. The Indians and the Eskimos were recognized as rightful sharers in the progress of their own land. Today natives sit in the legislative halls at Juneau, helping to shape the destiny of the forty-ninth state.

Their path had been prepared for them by a man who achieved greatness in his own way—Hudson Stuck "Archdeacon of the Yukon and to the Arctic Regions."

Suggestions For Further Reading About Alaska

Suggestions For Further Reading About Alaska

Browne, Belmore. *The Conquest of Mount McKinley*. Houghton Mifflin Co., Boston, Mass., 1956.

Herron, Edward A. *Alaska: Land of Tomorrow*. McGraw Hill Book Co., New York, 1947.

———. *Dimond of Alaska:* Adventurer in the Far North, Julian Messner, Inc., New York, 1957.

———. *First Scientist of Alaska: William Healey Dall*. Julian Messner, Inc., New York, 1958.

Stuck, Hudson. *Ten Thousand Miles with a Dog Sled,* Charles Scribner's Sons, New York, 1914.

———. *The Ascent of Denali (Mount McKinley)*. Charles Scribner's Sons, New York, 1914.

———. *Voyages on the Yukon and its Tributaries*. Charles Scribner's Sons, New York, 1917.

———. *A Winter Circuit of Our Arctic Coast*. Charles Scribner's Sons, New York, 1920.

Schwatka, Frederick. *Along Alaska's Great River*. Henry Publishing Co., Chicago, Ill., 1898.

Index

Index

Index

185

About the Author

EDWARD A. HERRON was born June 5, 1912 in Philadelphia, Pennsylvania. After graduation from St. Joseph's College, he shipped out as a merchant seaman. Then with royalties from a book published during undergraduate days, he headed for Alaska where he worked in the gold mines. During this period he started selling short stories and articles, mostly dealing with Alaska. While traveling and researching there, he came across the names of men who had come to Alaska to help the raw, uncharted country and wrote their stories in biographies for young people. Mr. Herron and his wife, with their children who were born in Alaska, now live in California.